Ms King —

May our light
continue to brighten
as we go forward
in our Awakening —
Much love & Endless Blessings
to you and your family

Gwyn Gorg
2021
www.gwyngorg.com

DARLENE'S AWAKENING

GWYNDOLIN GORG

DARLENE'S AWAKENING

WRITTEN BY
GWYNDOLIN GORG

ILLUSTRATIONS BY
SUNNY GORG & SEKAYA GORG-VERBURG

ISBN 978-0-578—79239-2
Library of Congress Control Number TXu 2-225-169

To the loving memory of my husband of 57 years

Alan Kent Gorg
1931-2021

and to my daughter

Galyn Gorg
1964-2021

Dedicated to:

The lost ones whose directions have been skewed as they attempt to understand life's mysteries; the confused who grasp tightly to dogmas while searching for solace to a troubled heart that promises everlasting delight; Others who traverse great distances mentally or spiritually in the hope of a more congenial acceptance.

Some who have quietly suffered abuse, physical, mental or verbal, and accepted the victim's role resulting in fear which erodes a connection to the intrinsic power that lies within each of us by not allowing objective introspection to unfold. The frightened who never venture beyond their familiar comfort zones for fear of the unknown as they limit their inherent participation in life's journey.

Those who have been easily influenced and accepted pejorative judgmental opinions because of their lack of a sense of self-honor; it is dedicated to anyone who has had to endure demeaning circumstances beyond their defined job descriptions; ones who distance themselves with a shield of superiority when in their private moments the accoutrements of an insecure person are exposed. Dedicated to the carriers of heavily burdened hearts; it is for some who are dissolving blockages that can hinder a person from asserting the power of love for themselves and for those who have learned the sweetness of forgiveness.

The Ones whose examples provide hope for others to ascribe to while representing the decency that prevails.

Personal experiences are determiners in choosing which direction will be taken. If a clear vision has not been embraced, accepted obstacles appear real, blocking one's true identity.

The acknowledgement of one's continual improvement, one's authenticity, the acceptance of self-love, are primary necessities in the quest for true Awakening

Table of Contents

AN INTRODUCTION

DARLENE'S AWAKENING is the story of a younger, adult, Negro Female as she evolved from a sheltered, naïve and inexperienced person in the 1950s. The repetitive life experiences in the familiar environment she had grown accustomed to were accepted without question. In a remote area of her unraveling, she was aware there was more in store for her than what seemed obvious as she participated in her daily routine. Venturing beyond familiar locations in her imagination offered inviting exploration. The promise of change, the possibility of new experiences was awaiting her discovery. She knew her desires were available, but had not the slightest idea of when, where or how they would manifest. Her religious training, her place in society as a second-place citizen, the role she had been assigned like many of her peers had been accepted without question. One of the legacies of slavery was religion and the Negro Community was inculcated with devout beliefs. Evidentiary indications were apparent as Negro female domestics who crossed the BAILEY on their bus ride each day in route to their various destinations with faces buried in their Bibles. Their holy books were major crutches that many clung to while searching for a realization that offered freedom from anguish. Other buttresses may have been available but were not as apparent. Attempting to hold onto that which promised a better future, their Bibles offered unquestioned assistance as Colored females faced their day-to- day obligations. Some of the obligatory duties went beyond their apparent job description.

.

The teachings Darlene had unconsciously taken for granted offered a degree of inner conflict when she was forced to question her life more intensely. Unexpected events propelled her into a different direction, created introspection that revealed new opportunities

The BAILEY bridge which was crossed in a westerly direction by countless Domestics and other blue-collar workers, offered a powerful metaphor of the separation that occurs between people. It was very similar to borders that separate vast numbers of citizens all over the world. Crossing the bridge in one direction represented financial stability, false illusions of superiority. In a westerly direction as the BAILEY was crossed there was a privileged acceptance for some, whether real or imagined, automatically inherited since childhood.

The opposite route where financial challenges became the norm and perhaps false illusions of inferiority were accepted by a large percentage. As the bus transported blue-collar workers to their places of employment an entirely different world where possibilities of order and manicured consciousness prevailed in many situations placing blame and not facing up to one's own participation whether consciously or unconsciously, causes us to dishonor our self-loyalty and block our own authenticity. contrast to some whose continuous fight for a more balanced life was a battle.

For young Darlene who was to learn truths which were paramount in the quest for self-respect and self-love which is minimized when the role of victim is accepted. In

A sizable number of older or retired workers, who lived east of the BAILEY and accepted a "less than," kind of existence, rather than confront some of life's challenges, sat on their porches, watched the passersby and became vicarious observers. Darlene's vision for her future would not have allowed her to be a passive witness who watched life pass by.

Patience, forgiveness and identifying solutions are tools that become necessary in the path to AWAKENING. Without being mindful or accepting responsibility of our own participation, it becomes a convenient way in which to lose sight of one's true self. If a true AWAKENING, is to manifest, we must assume some responsibility for every encounter we are involved in.

Darlene ventured outside accustomed boundaries, opened to an uncharted freshness and was surprised beyond her imagination.

REMEMBERING

*into the timeless realms of existence where the infinite
resides
an overview of newly discovered possibilities
as time collides into an unexplainable brilliance
illumining the passageway for vistas unknown
lost in the search for the meaning of the eternal
awaiting incoming revelations
where a continuity redefines itself
searching for answers as winds pluck
the strings of the universe connecting
to melodies that transport one beyond the reasonable
to uncluttered scenarios where no chaos resides
walking, skipping, whirling in circles
tip toeing on the surface of the true self with a delicate
connection
in the direction of the unspoken chants
I remember, I remember
to embrace a beautiful essence
that resides within
I remember. I remember, I remember*

First Chapter

I REMEMBER

JUNTEENTH

Darlene Annie Taylor was the name I was given on the day of my birth, May 28, 1933. A magical, mysterious unfolding of love, forgiveness, patience and understanding have been given to me as I have continued my evolution on this planet; a degree of responsibility to share some of the influences that pushed me to a more detailed understanding of my purpose is the story I will share.

East of the BAILEY, a typical afternoon; clear-blue sky; sporadic shape- shifting clouds following the morning rain which had calmed down the dust where we shared our annual Juneteenth celebration. The park was crowded with folks, mostly Negroes and a splattering of Mexicans, Chinese and some Whites who lived in the community. Couples holding hands, wheelchairs giving assistance to those in need and an occasional drunk were all in attendance on this special day. Children with their cotton candy faces outlined with a mixture of dirt and anything else that adhered to the sticky, gluey substance left by the moist sugar, were running and shouting while playing tag or hide and seek. Teenagers, thinking they had escaped the watchful eyes of adults were in secluded areas, kissing and tempting nature. The smell of barbecue penetrated the area. Sausages and ribs released smells that could not be resisted. An always integral part of the food-offerings were watermelon and strawberry soda because their red colors represented the blood that had been lost during slavery.

The continuous music each year, since I could remember, was always provided by the six musicians of the Gates of Yates Band who performed on the platform. Once the band had warmed up and rhythms alerting the crowd's sleeping cells to attention, feet could be seen tapping to the beat; fingers snapping; heads bobbing. It was usually at that warm- up point that some of the jitter-buggers jumped on the stage; twisting, gyrating, spinning, kicking, swinging, and on and on and on. In all directions, the feet of younger and older dancers, and non-dancers were keeping rhythm and with smiling faces.

From one year to the next, the identical musical selections were performed. Everyone seemed to enjoy the yearly repetition and requested the same songs. As if a new Freedom, a new experience for the first-time had been granted, the singer burst into a familiar rendition with the accompaniment of the audience. It was always the same, an undefinable, unshackled energy that could not be restrained, burst forth. The large gatherings, the intensity of the sound provided by the continuous music helped to create a joy-filled atmosphere that replaced daily mundane concerns and obligations. A penetrating vitality was shared at this annual event. The day offered a safe and a secure environment where the community relaxed. For a brief period, laughter, lies and prayers were all present. Problems vanished and solutions were possible.

This day offered, special memories. Abraham Lincoln had signed the Emancipation Proclamation in 1863; however, some areas chose to ignore the ending of slavery. Two years later on June 19, 1865, the Union officer, General Granger and his soldiers rode into Galveston, Texas and enforced the official ending of slavery. Every year on this day, referred to as Juneteenth, Colored people celebrated.

DARLENE'S AWAKENING

ANTHONY `1952

On this particular 1952 afternoon, there was a buzz among the crowd, mostly the women, especially the younger adult ones talking about the tall, smooth, pecan -colored skin, easy to look at man who had recently come to town. His body language, the upward thrust of his chin, and the stride represented confidence. A clear memory remains with me of the first day I saw the handsome, young, single, Colored man who had entered our community. In addition to being polite, he offered a new perspective on a wide variety of topics. He appeared to have information on many subjects and was able to discuss whatever was being shared. To have knowledge about so many topics, I assumed he had traveled extensively. People who had become accustomed to the norm without ever having ventured into unexplored realms found his opinions stimulating. Everyone, especially the women noticed Anthony, the newcomer who had arrived in our neighborhood. Smart, polite, respectful, and very good-looking with a strong body build was he. This man seemed as if all of his dreams could happen.

His gorgeous smile, beautiful set of teeth and gentleness captured all parts of me. There was an immediate attraction. Our magnetic impulses drew us closer and closer until the force was too strong to release. We had become almost inseparable. Seven years older than I was my twenty- six, year old dream man. Even if I had wanted, there was no escape from him for me. After knowing each other for four months, we got married. Before Anthony arrived in Liston, mine was an unquestioned acceptance of most things I had learned. Going to work each day, being a loyal churchgoer, paying my tithes, and living a simple life were those things I had accepted. His entrance into my life with probing questions about various things I had taken for granted, the personal dissatisfaction he experienced daily, began to dismantle unsettled, moldy, musty thoughts that had corrupted my reality. A more elevated awareness has forced me to become more accountable.

19

Good Morning, good morning the repetitive mantra of the alarm clock signaled each day's beginning and interrupted a fulfilling embrace for Anthony and me. After making the bed and other basic requirements I would go into our small kitchen to prepare breakfast. Perhaps the kitchen was not so small, however, the working space had been severely reduced. My grandmother Betty's home was typical of lots of the dwellings in our neighborhood. She inherited the house many years ago. The complete details, I had never been privy to. The story as I understood was that it was given to her father, a sharecropper. At any rate, it was a two-story, mixed Craftsman-Victorian replica, beige with moss-green trim and an attic that housed items of every description. As I reflect back and having grown wiser, the realization that many of those objects must have had financial value could possibly have dissolved the financial deficits we had to face from time to time. An assortment of objects dated from the past century on shelves, in boxes, others hanging from hooks, some were laid across baskets. The abundance of stuff that had been stored and an oppressive, heavy, moldy odor that initiated continuous sneezing and caused my breathing to be compromised the few times I entered. There were lamps, a four-story dollhouse reminiscent of slavery-time plantation houses, velvet curtains, clothes of all descriptions, a treadle-sewing machine, a rocking chair, old-fashioned trunks that when opened displayed panels of drawers.

DARLENE'S AWAKENING

Several boxes of books captured my interest as I became older. Reading has always been where I was able to escape into a surprising awareness. It has brought me relief when life was sometimes burdensome. One of the boxes was labeled, Coloreds. Opening it revealed authors I was unfamiliar with. Of the writers I had a minimum knowledge of was Paul Lawrence Dunbar. Authors Langston Hughes, Zora Neal Hurston, W.E.B Dubois, Richard Wright, Ralph Ellison and James Baldwin I had never known about. What a surprise to learn they were Negroes who had interesting stories to tell. There were other writers who I had been introduced to in my high school classes, but none of them had been Colored. Some of the other boxes included books written by John Steinbeck, J.D. Salinger, Shakespeare and Mark Twain. Who were these people who had bestowed such books to Mama? Had I not developed an interest, perhaps they would have been buried in the midst of all the other boxes and never have been appreciated. These books have remained with me and are still referenced at times.

Going into the attic reminded Lorna and me of a strange and unappealing area therefore, we almost never ventured into it. When we were children, my sister told me there were three ghosts who lived in the attic and I should never go up there by myself. I asked her if she had ever seen a ghost in our attic, her answer was negative, but she assumed that would be the kind of place where ghosts would have lived. As I grew older, I didn't believe her report but still there was an uneasiness whenever I ventured into that space. My interest in reading and having vicarious experiences outweighed my fear of ghosts. Whenever I entered the attic, I looked and listened for strange intruders, none were ever seen. I would carefully and quietly enter the mysterious area searching for reading materials to take me to unknown worlds beyond my obvious existence.

There had been occasional mention of Grandma Betty opening a second-hand store, an idea that never materialized beyond discussion. Her shared goals were to eventually separate and donate many of the articles to different organizations. Mama Betty's daily demands overrode the call of organizing the upper level of her home, thus it became a depository for the continuous articles that were given to her. Why had people from west of the BAILEY chosen to share their discards with my grandmother? Sometimes, she complained but never did she refuse when cars arrived with boxes or bags of their give-ways. The larger discarded pieces Mama Betty inherited that were too cumbersome to go into the overflowing attic reduced the kitchen area to a minimum of space. The carved oak kitchen table could be extended to accommodate eight people comfortably, but we kept it collapsed to a minimum, which served four in order for enough space to be provided to get from the sink to the stove to the refrigerator. On the north facing wall was a French Provincial inlaid glass cabinet with a polished walnut frame supported by carved wooden legs that held various dishes on each shelf.

Many times, Mama Betty could be heard repeating how one day she would organize some of the clutter. I had often thought perhaps, there would be a time I would attempt to put things in a more orderly manner. My job as a Domestic helped me to have a clearer understanding about my grandmother's inability to better organize the immensity of materials she had been given. Arising early, cleaning another person's house every day from six to seven hours, finally arriving home to a place where there was a degree of freedom after taking my shoes off, and enjoying a relaxing shower, the desire for more organizing became a well thought out future idea. Our entire town had a population of one hundred fifty thousand. On the east side of the bridge where I lived, there were twenty- five thousand of us, mostly Negroes, the descendants of ex-slaves who had been brought to this town decades ago; few Mexicans; a sprinkling of Orientals; there was also a small group of Whites who had remained in this area even when their ancestors fled westward or to other destinations.

DARLENE'S AWAKENING

Once the BAILEY Bridge was crossed, which separated the east from the west the population was represented with only White people. Mama Betty, my grandmother's endearing name, seemed to have known people from our community and some from faraway. At her huge funeral, there were diverse races, young, old and even some Whites from west of the bridge.

LIFE'S SOULFUL MENUS

Most weekdays, the ordinary, not particularly interesting morning meal was prepared by me. It was a fairly typical and very basic breakfast consisting of toast, eggs, bacon, coffee or maybe oatmeal, an orange and coffee. I looked forward to the mornings when Anthony cooked, he got up before the alarm sounded, was in the kitchen as the sun came up making a meal of pancakes with fresh apple sauce or maybe grilled potatoes and onions, sausages, orange juice or some other delicious foods. Sunday was Anthony's primary day to exhibit his culinary skills, never was I disappointed with the menu. His prepared breakfast feast might consist of a big waffle platter, on a different day French toast with bananas and cream, another morning homemade biscuits or other breads made from scratch with fresh peach preserves, maybe one of the days boiled or baked grits with cheese and herbs. I can remember those times when he drove us across town to buy Canadian Bacon, according to him it was much better than the regular bacon everyone usually ate. Truthfully, I couldn't really tell the difference.

Of the many delicious meals Anthony made, a preference of mine was when he sliced a biscuit into equal halves, layered it with slices of Canadian bacon, topped with a softly cooked egg under a delicious yellowish sauce. The two recipe books he owned were from some of the gifts I had given him which apparently helped to inspire his creativity. Smoked sausages, extremely thin sliced strips of ham would sometimes be on the menu. Until I met Anthony, grits cooked in ways other than boiled were unfamiliar to me, the delicious egg offerings; omelets or poached I had never had.

The choices I had grown-up eating were either scrambled, hard boiled, and over-easy. In addition to the delicious meals he prepared, he made the entire setting visually pleasing. The table was covered with one of Grandma Betty's linen tablecloths and a complete place setting for each of us with a flower placed in the center of the table. He enjoyed cooking much more than I did. Family and friends who had the pleasure of feasting on his cookery suggested he share his gastronomic delights and have his own autonomous business. Discussions of owning a small restaurant surfaced from time to time, but there was never total commitment to the idea. His resistance to becoming his own boss and offering palate pleasing foods to customers was not easily understood by me.

When we met, it was if a special kind of glue bound us together. We were constantly teased about our closeness. Our four-year marriage represented a special connection, unique to us. Of the activities we shared together, attending church, was a solo endeavor, just for me. His comment many times was that, "God did not have much concern for Coloreds, especially Colored men."

DARLENE'S AWAKENING

Never had I heard anyone question God's motives the way he did. Sometimes his comments were very unsettling. Anthony did not deny the existence of a God Source. He was just unable to accept the teachings in the churches he had visited. His complaints were about the ministers who drove big, expensive new cars, the property they owned and the fancy jewelry that adorned many of them. Anthony used to say, "If they were so connected to God and were setting examples, why are their material possessions so important?" My defense of the Church Heads would encourage me to say," because they are leaders, their congregation is supposed to support them and desires the best for them. "Darlene, that's a stupid argument when there are so many poor people who go to church every Sunday and can barely support themselves and their families." We were generally unable to move forward in our discussion. Attempting to convince him otherwise created disharmony, therefore, we agreed not to discuss religion.

Each Sunday when I returned home from church, the dishes had been washed and put away, the trash had been taken out and everything was in order. Possibly, because he was the only boy in a family with three female siblings, he learned to do chores around the house that are generally ascribed to females. I did not know how or why, but I was grateful. Saturday and Sunday afternoons and evenings we spent together and had dedicated those times for our own special plans. Each weekend was set aside for uninterrupted togetherness as our love grew stronger and we gave more attention to each other.

There were those occasions when Anthony would cite all the abuse Negro men had endured. Each time he got laid off from his employment, he was assured it was because there was no one who really cared, and especially God. He had had twelve different jobs in our four-year marriage. The first few months of each job, he seemed happy but always with the idea it probably would not work out. His perceived attitude, his acceptance of defeat appeared to wait in the sidelines for the opportunity to emphasize his rejection. This expected denial became a catalyst that scraped his sensitivity and gave him permission to fight back, by walking away from that which he felt was beyond his control.

Various types of work Anthony had experienced: A night watchman, assistant gardener, a custodian, a chauffeur, a dishwasher, a door–to–door salesman and a delivery person are some of the positions he had held. His job as a delivery person ended abruptly when the dispatcher gave him the wrong address. It was the one that pulled the boulders from his foundation. He arrived 45 minutes later than expected and once he returned to headquarters, the boss fired him on the spot without allowing him the courtesy of an explanation. He blamed the incident on his race and abandonment by God. I encouraged him not to give up and reminded him of all of his skills and how smart he was. "What does smart have to do with it?" He would reply. "I know I am smart and all those things you say, but don't you understand, I am a Colored man in a White world and God just doesn't give a damn. He must have created us to be the workers or something worse. Why must our entire race have to be treated with such disregard Darlene?"

When he was so agitated, I had no answer. The man who had entered our area offering such a vision of confidence seemed to have vanished. Perhaps, our closeness, our familiarity with each other allowed a truer representation of his vulnerabilities. He was not the person I had become magnetized to. He seemed to have a menu of rejections to choose from, depending on the circumstances. There was always a reason to blame others. Anthony was an amazingly talented, polite, and a kind person. I was aware of the racial disrespect he had endured. My uncles, cousins and other male relatives told of similar mistreatments, but they coped differently. I was familiar with inequality, racism existed but as a female who stayed within the boundaries, it was not as evident. The invisibility I had grown accustomed to, like many provided topics for discussion at church dinners or family gatherings. I wanted to offer solace to my beloved, but I didn't know how to. He did not easily accept my offerings.

DARLENE'S AWAKENING

There were times his sister and I had telephone conversations and spoke about his unhappiness. She told me he had been miserable since their dad and mother divorced when they were teenagers. She said, "Anthony was constantly looking for something far away that he was unable to access." She also said his family was very happy when he and I got married because for a time they thought he had found a bit of happiness. Those rare times when everything was going well in his life, he would display that beautiful smile and we laughed and played like children do.

When he quit his job as a chauffeur I did not know if I wanted to congratulate him or remind him of the necessity of both of us having employment in order to move ahead in the directions we had planned for our future. According to Anthony, as he arrived to pick up the four passengers, on of them shouted, "the Nigger is here." He attempted to ignore their comments, as they got in the car, continuously referring to him as the Nigger. Did they not think of him as an individual with sensitivities, a human being, a man? Was their ignorance at such a low level they were behaving their best? Their treatment of him was as if he did not exist as if his feelings were of no concern to them. Anthony chose to be quiet, drove them to another part of town opposite from where their final destination would have been. He pulled up to a dark street corner in the industrial section on the east side of the BAILEY, removed the keys, got out of the car and walked away. The shouting as he walked away was heard for several blocks. Needless to say, that job ended. It was a dignified way in which my husband found a non-violent and a safe way to have some self-respect.

Often Anthony shared the hurt and pain he had to deal with each day as a Negro man; the many times, he had to remain quiet when he did not agree with the words uttered by his White boss; the times in which he felt less than a man; the evenings when walking home alone where he had to be careful not to be on back isolated streets for fear of never returning home. When I told him about having faith, he reminded me of the injustices Colored people have endured; about how the knees were tender, sensitive, and rough with scars because of kneeling so many years asking for justice and equality.

Second Chapter

EAST TO WEST

DOMESTICS...CHOSEN ONES...INVISIBLES

No matter the state of the weather: rain might be beating down upon the earth with roaring thunder like the pounding of a drum or unbearably, hot summertime when the sun's uncomfortable heat, burns and burns.

At exactly seven fifty-five on weekdays, I walked to the bus stop passing the homes of my retired senior citizen neighbors who were perched in stationary configurations on their front porches high above the sidewalk. It was of interest to me as to how early they arose, because each of them appeared to have been sitting in their exact locations forever, never in different positions. This daily routine was perhaps one of the highlights of their day. I remember thinking how boring it was to arrive at a point in one's life and the most interesting thing was to sit on the porch and observe neighborhood action.

When I got to the bus stop, Mrs. Gertrude Wilson on the opposite side of the street was always in her yard caring for her pale-colored Hydrangea plants. From my side of the street, they never appeared especially attractive, in fact, some looked as if they did not get enough water. Perhaps her plants were too crowded, because they certainly looked as if they needed more than they were receiving. In comparison to some of her peers sitting on their porches watching the days morph into months and the months change to years until finally the curtain closed, at least she was actively involved in life.

I assumed waving and shouting good morning to me must have been an important part of her daily routine because there were days when she rushed from the back of her house to acknowledge me just before the bus arrived. Usually, she wore work gloves, a bonnet and an apron with gardening tools. I had never been in her backyard. I always supposed she had a garden that thrived and demanded much of her time. For many years, Mrs. Wilson and my grandmother were friends who attended the same church. The special obligation she had towards me each morning must have been directly connected to their relationship. Precisely, one minute each day after our greeting ritual, the bus arrived as if a mechanical force was controlling our interaction.

At exactly 8:05 am, the same bus driver smiled at me and I to him. We never exchanged many words, just a typical daily greeting. Pete was the name revealed on his identification badge, nothing more. After the four of us who got on at my bus stop were seated, the bus proceeded to the next stops where from that point on, it began to fill up until there was standing room only. For the past years of riding this bus each day, numerous variations were provided but still many similarities. I believed if I became involved in the passenger's personal stories, I would experience much confusion; therefore, I chose to look out the window at the passing scenery

At the corner of Olive and Nelson, usually four to six older men were seated on boxes or crates very involved in their activities. Most days four or five were Negroes and two others were Mexican. I imagined these men sharing tales as they played dominoes and had endless stories discarded in their memories. They had each other to lend support to. Were they married? Did they have children? Had they given up? When they were as young as Anthony, were they as angry as he was as he tried to unravel his life? Were they also disappointed with God? I was certain if ever the opportunity presented itself, perhaps I would ask them some of these questions. Did the fact that they represented two different races provide them similar outlooks?

DARLENE'S AWAKENING

The long bus ride each day provided a platform for me to investigate, explore and question some of the many concerns that were constantly in my head. This was my personal and private mental dialogue that occurred each day as I pondered and attempted to sort out some of the mysteries as a Colored woman.

As the bus continued westward, small businesses lined the street, Beauty shops, Barber shops and a Pawn Shop with bold gold lettering advertising the best deal west of the Mississippi. Mr. Thomas' Tool Sharpening and Machine shop gained my interest the most because it was different from all the other businesses on the street. Its exterior was a shiny silver almost aluminum color. Never had I seen a color of its kind in our community. It was another of those curiosities I wondered about. Where had he been able to acquire such a unique color? As a customer entered the store, he would ask, are you sharp or dull? Without waiting for an answer, his robust laughter was infectious. He was jovial and usually shared a joke. Mr. Thomas told me when he was younger, he had wanted to be a comedian because he loved to make people laugh and according to him, laughter would save the world. When he got married and began having children, he was faced with a different reality and was smart enough to know that making people laugh as a comedian here in our small town, would probably not be the way to make a decent living. Mr. Thomas' uncle had taught him how to sharpen tools and repair small motors when he was a young boy. Those skills had helped to prepare him to have his own business. He sharpened lawnmowers, hoes, rakes, saws, even scissors, and knives. Mr. Thomas could fix sewing machines, or anything with a small operating device. In addition to repairing items, he sold animal food for cats, dogs, birds, ducks and chickens. His slogan was, Enter Dull, Exit Sharp. He loved his slogan. People from east or west of the BAILEY brought their tools to him. Numerous customers exited his shop with smiles on their faces.

Peering out the windows for several blocks as the bus continued along, two or three store-front churches were apparent on both sides of the street. Anthony said, "if religion was the answer, then the large numbers of churches represented would preclude any suffering in our community. Why is it that with all of those churches Colored men are still being hanged and some Ku Klux Klan members are in high positions in government? It doesn't make sense Darlene." He would repeat, "these damn churches just help people to hold onto their slave acceptance as second place citizens." I remember thinking it was probably a good thing that Mama Betty was dead because for her to hear some of Anthony's views about the church and God would have upset her very much. I doubt she had ever questioned any of these possibilities.

The bus passed Cotto's Café and Market with the sign "You Buy, We Fry." This business had the strongest impact as it titillated senses with its smells of fish, onions and garlic. Once the bus approached the café and after passing it for a few blocks, the aromas remained. This particular geographical location is often identified by its unique smell. Did the employees have these odors embedded in their clothes?

Several years of riding the bus with the same people offered nothing new or interesting. I had wished many times my life would in some way be a surprise, something wonderfully unexpected to replace the everyday tedium. Having no idea what it would be but a change that might unlock a longing just waiting to reveal itself. A longing for what, I did not know.

My familiarity on this daily bus ride allowed me the ability to close my eyes and know who would enter or who would exit at each stop. For some of the daily riders, I knew what their attire would be on a particular day.

DARLENE'S AWAKENING

On Tuesdays, the short chubby man wearing a khaki shirt with matching pants might have been in his forties generally carried a stuffed brown-paper bag, a book, and a thermos. Never did he open the book. What was he reading about? Were there sandwiches in his bag? Was there coffee, tea or some other stimulating drink in his thermos? I wondered. In my years of riding this same bus five days a week, never had I observed a smile or an appearance of his being totally present or any kind of interaction with another person. He reminded me of a disembodied person, floating about unaware of those around him. The more I thought about what his story might have been, the more I realized I didn't honestly want to know. He seemed mysterious to me, maybe he was just a lonely, scared and an unhappy person. Generally, he stared straight ahead, with a strange, weird look, in fact a little scary to me. I wondered if the other riders experienced him the way I did. He never seemed to be aware of others on the bus and from my observation no one interacted with him. It was as if he was one of the invisibles.

The day he boarded and chose the seat next to me, my prayer as he was approaching was that he would locate another place to sit. The prayer did not work. There were other seats available, why did this seemingly weird character choose to sit next to me? As he was preparing to sit down, our eyes met, I smiled but there was no return acknowledgement. The look in his eyes reminded me of a hand–held drill that could bore a hole deep into the receiver or perhaps a body devoid of a soul. Not really knowing how to define what I was attempting to understand prompted me to look away from him immediately because the strange-eyed stare made him appear inhuman and creepy. Never did he utter a sound, just continued with his strange focus and a smell of liniment and sage. It was the scent that had been rubbed on my chest when I had the flu. It was an odor that made me feel nauseous. Looking out of the window while attempting to control my breath in order not to throw up and embarrass myself. Again, in my private, inner conversation I was asking myself, why did this weird, and very strange man choose to sit next to me? It was a most uncomfortable bus ride. I began counting the bus stops hoping this journey would end fast. On this particular day, it seemed as if time had slowed down. It was if each stop was longer than usual and people lingered as they entered or exited the bus.

Mrs. Birdie Crocker who had been secretly tagged as "TGR, the Gossip Reporter," in our community was seated across the aisle from me observing my dilemma with an expression of empathy. For another twenty minutes, sitting side-by side this khaki-clad stranger and I rode along in silence. I wondered about this man who had sat next to me, stared ahead, never uttered a sound, never opened his brown bag, never opened the book he was carrying, never took a drink from his thermos. It was difficult to know if he was going to or coming from work. Why didn't he move to another seat? I might have moved to a different location, but I did not want to attract attention. Had I not felt so strange and not had so much farther to go, I would have stood up. My discomfort became so magnified that I turned my back away from him and observed the passing scenery more intently.

At stop number 4, five people boarded. The one woman's attire; a handbag, a scarf, dress, stockings and shoes each day were always black. Judging from her facial expression, much sadness outweighed her joy.

The main reason I waited until the last five minutes to rush to the bus stop each morning was to avoid having to listen to Miss Birdie, TGR who had words to share about everyone within a five- mile radius of our block. According to her report, the woman who wore all black was in mourning because her husband and two children were accidentally killed in an automobile accident. Perhaps, it was true, perhaps not. Interestingly, TGR had bits of information about almost everyone, but never shared anything concerning the seemingly mysterious, khaki-clad man. My sister Lorna who also knew many of the secret tales in our community reminded me not to believe most of Miss Birdies reports. According to Lorna, Birdie sometimes adds her own version to make the story more interesting. Miss TGR also shared that the single younger woman who boarded the bus at stop number five with her three little girls, was a single mother and each of the kids had a different father. Rather than becoming involved in the daily gossip I attempted to avoid her reports each morning by leaving home at an exact moment and timing the precise arrival of the bus in order not to have to wait at the bus stop and become involved in the morning's hearsay.

DARLENE'S AWAKENING

Four stops before this bus # K-621 heading in a westerly direction crossed the BAILEY Bridge was where Angel Harp entered the bus. Her demeanor was very different from most of the female Negro Domestic Workers going to their places of employment with profound lines on their faces indicating rejection, fear and depression. The lines seemed to have been chiseled in deeply and permanently on the faces of some of these women whose facial features indicated those who looked much older than their true chronological ages. These workers traveled across town, distances from their familiarity to cook, clean, iron, be a wet nurse and perform other unassigned job duties. Rarely did smiles occur as some of the women could be observed almost burying their heads in the pages of their bibles, one of the crutches that supported their confusion, their loneliness and strengthened their belief in eternal salvation. I had no idea about this salvation. Was it somewhere that would be accessible in the future? Had my grandmother or some of the other ancestors relocated to this dwelling? Would it be the place represented in the song "No More Weeping and a Wailing, going home to live with God," a possible dream where all troubles were no more? Were their lives so knotted up with despair that accessing a happier future life was a reality worth planning and waiting for? As I rode the bus and each day observing the daily passengers, their lack of … , sometimes saddened me. I do not even know what the lack was, but there definitely appeared to be an absence of happiness, lightness, smiles, and joy. It was usually an atmosphere filled with quietness and solemnity. The long, daily bus ride provided an opportunity for me to have moments of reflection.

Most of my life, I had heard Colored women talk about being saved, and one day living as a chosen one. Anthony used to laugh at the concept of a chosen one and he would repeat, "yeah, chosen to clean up after some low-life, bow down and stay in the background. Well, Darlene, you go on to church so that you can prepare for the day you will also become a chosen one." He would laugh and laugh. I thought I understood many of the concepts, but the more I learned, and the more my husband presented his probing disclaimers that caused me for the first time in my life to stop accepting ideas without more information. Another of the burdens some of these women accepted was the persistent reminder of the ascribed role of "less than."

The almost docile beliefs some of these ladies accepted was never easily received by me. I had understood myself as a blessed one, because my Grandma, Mama Betty had assured me since I was a little girl that I was as good as anyone and maybe better than some. She told me, "being Colored might make your life more difficult, but I want you to know you have much to offer and must never, ever consider yourself less than anyone." She constantly shared this perspective with my sister Lorna and me. The older I have become, the better I have understood some of her wisdom.

In the mid to late fifties, television had begun to play a major part in many of the local households. There were no roles to elevate Colored people. Sometimes Amos and Andy two bungling businessmen presented a slap-stick version of Negro life. Hattie Mc Daniels as Beulah the endearing, subservient, typical Domestic was popular. The roles were extremely limited and if Negro women had an opportunity to work as actresses, the only available roles offered were those of, subservient, demeaning characters. The darker-skinned, overweight females who could offer a cultural sarcasm represented a stereotype that was considered an acceptable norm. The portrayals of success, and beauty were not the roles depicting Colored females.

Many Negro women let go of their innermost emotions by shouting or crying out in church and releasing feelings to the good Lord. For some it was the only thing that helped to prevent them from an eventual breakdown. Shouting in some Christian Churches was acceptable behavior for those who claim to have the Holy Ghost, it was a way for certain women who had the need for a gratifying discharge to feel okay. Was their loud crying and jumping about an adequate release for a group who did not solicit the assistance of a psychologist or a psychiatrist? Colored people did not use those kinds of services. The Minister or Preacher was the person to take troubles to. Usually, the general idea was if you went to a "shrink," the reference was that you were "crazy." In addition to other disclaimers, that was not an acceptable label in the Negro community. Also, there was usually no extra money to afford their services. Had they agreed to the idea that for a Black, suffering is inevitable and only a loud demonstrative prayer would give some relief?

DARLENE'S AWAKENING

My broad consent of some church doctrine had never been total and listening to Anthony caused me to question even more intently. I attended church most Sundays because I had been trained and introduced to it since I was a child. Church was taken for granted and whatever we were taught, we consented to without hesitation. It became one of the legacies of Slavery, the one place where large groups of slaves were permitted to congregate. The continuation of this concept has carried on to modern times. Sunday church service for some Negroes became the social event of the week. Hats, gloves, shined shoes, pressed hair, manicured nails and the latest styles were paraded about each Sunday. It was the one place away from pejorative employers with their superior attitudes where some Coloreds were exposed to a freedom that existed no place else. At Sunday church service none of us were the invisibles, domestics, housekeepers, chauffeurs, butlers, or maids. Prominent postures strong and upright were on display. We had a place to parade, to model our Sunday attire but more than anything, we felt beautiful and safe. From those earlier days, the influence of the church has continued, primarily for the female descendants. The minister's words were gifts from God and total acceptance was required in order to be saved. As a child I had many unanswered questions, but was told, the Preacher was the one who had an unaltered interpretation of God's message.

When Anthony and I married, many more unanswered questions sprang forth. His concerns and doubts about church, the minister, and religion were reasonable to me, causing me to investigate some of the subject matter more intensely than I had ever thought about. Much of the interrogation about religion Anthony put forth prompted me to have reservations and probe more deeply in ways I may never have considered in the past. The long bus ride each day provided time for a soulful, mental investigation regarding the many puzzles that occupied my private curiosity. There had been mornings as I was deeply committed to my thoughts while endeavoring to unravel them, as our westerly Bound Bus# K-621, four stops from the BAILEY Bridge opened its doors. and passenger Angel Harp, a tall attractive medium- brown skinned woman with picture perfect skin entered and interrupted whatever thoughts or other experiences had been taking place before she boarded. Her demeanor was very different from the typical female Colored Domestics. The confidence she displayed was that of a person who had been used to being in front of groups of people.

Similar to many of those workers who carried large bags with their personal belongings, she was no exception. The difference was she carried three large hand–woven fabric bags, a purple, a cobalt-blue and a green one, embroidered with designs of flowers, triangles, circles and other motifs I was very unfamiliar with. Her carrier did not look like the typical ones sold in our local stores. I wondered if she had traveled to other places. Sometimes the colors of these bags were in deep contrast to the very bright colors she wore. Those days she wore all red with a pink and chartreuse scarf, provided a visual experience that made the eyes blink many times. Her daily attire, reminiscent of a showgirl from the early forties with ruffles and laces adorning her long-sleeved blouses, usually aroused those who were in a state of slumber. The skirts were generally ankle length, made from cotton, corduroy, occasionally velvet or another shiny material I was unable to identify.

DARLENE'S AWAKENING

She paid her fare, acknowledged Pete and in the flash of a moment took complete control of all activity on the bus. In a loud voice she would address passengers from the front of the bus to the back, asking? "Have you been saved? Have you been reading your bible?" No one ever replied, and she always repeated, "Almighty God loves all of us." Most times people attempted to ignore her, but could be observed stealing looks when they felt she was not focusing in their direction. Her voice grew very rhythmical and louder, as she became more involved in her delivery. When Angel got exceptionally loud, it was as if she were preaching a sermon, even when the bus was very crowded as it generally was before it crossed the bridge. Pete, the driver echoed the same words each day "Calm down Angel," she would laugh. "Pete, you get a blessing too." This became her pulpit, her platform, her stage where she delivered a very dogmatic discourse each morning. After careful thought, I realized she must have given lots of preparation to her speeches because each day they referenced different aspects of bible quotations, but always with a similar theme. The regulars, those who rode this particular bus every morning, could be seen looking out their windows before the bus stopped for her to get on. Even those passengers who had been standing could be seen leaning over to get a better visual image out of a window before she entered. Everyone seemed to await her arrival and prepare for the daily amusement each morning. Angel did not represent a quiet personality type, and seemed unaffected, or intimidated by anyone, regardless of race, religion or anything that might separate people. It was impossible to know if some of the riders agreed or disagreed with her diatribe. Whatever their opinions, they probably would have remained quiet for fear of being embarrassed.

Looking at this woman and imagining her past provided daily entertainment and endless curiosity for myself and other passengers.

The day, the strange man who wore all khaki clothes sat next to me, he did not move or make utterances of any kind as Angel made her pronouncements. He continued to stare ahead without any body movements. This was his typical behavior each day as she boarded the bus. Did he ever react to anything or anyone?

According to the stories in circulation, a major storm happened several years ago and if not by the Grace of God, Angel would have been killed. The prevailing accepted story was the Lord called her to get up and go into the kitchen for a glass of water. At that precise instant when she had gotten out of her bed to go into the kitchen for a glass of water, one of the big Oak trees toppled, crashed through the roof and landed on her bed, directly on the pillow where she would have been lying. Unprecedented amounts of precipitation entered through the roof and the windows, the house became flooded, but rescuers saved her just in time. Is this true, perhaps yes, perhaps no, it is the rendition Miss TGR shares. She also reports that Angel had been some kind of entertainer in another country, maybe a singer or a dancer she did not know for sure, in addition she shared that Angel was not the true name. Her given name was Doris and the family name Raye. How and where Miss TGR obtained so much information was bewildering? I wondered, was she a secret, private detective or just a lonely woman prying into other people's lives? Could it be that TGR was one who desperately needed an audience? She knew information about almost every occurrence on the east side of the bridge, ironically, not much was known about her.

PIECE OF PERFECTION

I am an intrinsic part of the universe blood
flowing through my veins, the same as kings, queens
salt in my tears as alkaline as seas that wash the shores
shades of my skin like the dark chocolate that sweetens the
palate as bright as the sunshine sparkling on the white
sand
curly hair that twists and shrivels as the weather demands
you who choose to ignore me as a first- class human
sometimes treat me as if I do not exist
your true essence shrouded in a web of uncertainty.
My invisibility to you is but your fantasy
Each of us a part of life's puzzle
together we bind the pieces
I am you……you are me
I am an on-purpose piece of perfection
and so are you

Third Chapter

THE BAILEY

LINE OF DEMARCATION

Suddenly the words from Angel and the chatter from the other passengers was silenced, everything came to a standstill, The BAILEY always took center stage. This Bridge is a familiar landmark to everyone in our area. People refer to their locations in references to the bridge, i.e., I live four blocks north of the BAILEY, I am about a mile from the BAILEY." It is exactly in the middle of town extending over the Sanderson River which is approximately 75 feet from shore to shore. The Suspension Bridge supported by large steel cables had a tendency to gently sway. I referred to the bridge as taking center stage, because the time seemed irrelevant whether it was day or night, early or very late, once the busses front tires touched it, everyone, everything gave the impression of being frozen. The only sounds heard were the vibrations and rattling noises emanating from the metal supports as each tire connected directly to the bridge. Those riders, who had been napping, became alert with eyes wide open, some of us had prayerful moments, others paused their breaths until we crossed to the other side. The bus and the BAILEY connected while demanding a quiet reverence from the passengers. The river below gently curved and twisted revealing white caps after a storm. During the rainy season, it rose and rushed violently. Years ago, a huge storm ravaged our area and for weeks afterwards, remnants of two houses were visible, floating downstream as the bus made its daily route.

Most passengers became extremely quiet each time the bus crossed over the river. Lorna reminded me not to be afraid because of an article in the newspaper that had been written by the Mayor, which gave assurance of the bridge's safety. Angel Harp did not have much to say as the bus crossed over; however, as soon as the bus reached the other side, her declarations would again resume as if she had guided everyone to the west side of the river to safety.

Abruptly, the landscape changed and the contrast was very revealing. On the west side, of the river, the street opened up to four lanes rather than the two lanes on the east side that caused traffic jams. The view out the window on the southside revealed pasture lands with cattle grazing. On the northside was where Golden Dreams is located, the massive cemetery reserved for Whites which sits at the top of the hill with its beautifully maintained lawns. At the entrance, is an attractive, refreshing scene surrounded by flowers with a fountain that shoots water up a few feet and cascades down into a pool. Sometimes the wind-blown fragrances would waft into the confines of the bus. Except for the sadness that must have been deposited there it could have been very inviting. An older man friend of my grandmother used to be employed at that cemetery. He was the only Colored person I had ever known who entered there. From my vantage point on the bus Golden Dreams looked like it might be a pleasant resting place.

DARLENE'S AWAKENING

As the bus continued along its route, Jubilee Park came into view with its large trees that give shade and comfort on the hot summer days when unbearable, uncomfortable temperatures penetrated to the core. Looking in the direction of the park, I drifted into a daydream imagining families having picnics, eating corn-on-the cob, children flying kites and everyone just having a good time. Large Oaks releasing their acorns, Willows bending as if giving homage to the earth and Sycamore trees providing a border that surrounded most of the park, supplying shade but in addition were beautiful. Peering out the window of the bus, barely visible in the distance was a lake. I imagined the relief one found in an area so welcoming. The key difference between this park and Owens Park on my side of town were the trees. Owens Park east of the BAILEY had Large Oleander bushes, some Oaks that adorned the landscape and a few picnic tables. Because of the reduction of trees during those hottest days, people in my community waited until approximately two 0'clock in the afternoon to go to the park as the intensity of the heat simmered down. Once, a neighbor child had to be rushed to the hospital as a result of putting a poisonous Oleander flower into her mouth and chewing it. Why would poisonous plants be grown in an area where families congregate? I had never considered the question until Anthony proposed it to me. He also told me, "the Black politicians who could make things better are only interested in making money, and don't really care about their people. They were probably all attending some church together on Sundays pontificating with open palms awaiting donations, wearing their expensive clothes and exhibiting their hypocrisy."

Grazing horses and cattle roaming in pastures parallel to the road were another sight to enjoy just before the bus entered the residential area with its enormous houses. Many of these domiciles had large trees, fountains, flower gardens, and all of the extras that lend beauty to an environment. I pulled the cord to alert the bus driver to stop. The stranger who had been sitting next to me never uttered a sound, continued to stare ahead as I stood up and excused myself. I promised if ever he sat next to me again, I would find my courage and either stand or move to another seat.

As I was waiting for the bus to stop at my exit, I observed Angel Harp, the strange khaki-clad man who had sat next to me and a few other passengers and was curious as to where they went each day. I had never noticed them acknowledging or talking to each other. Did they work at the same location? These people were never present on the return afternoon bus as were most of the other early morning passengers. The few who traveled beyond this point were somewhat mysterious to me and my curiosity was heightened because they did not fit the typical profile as Domestics. The bus stop where I exited was the farthest west I had ever been.

INVISIBLES

I was the youngest of the six of us who used to exit the bus on Clarington Way. Bessie and Bruce Mason, the older married couple entered through the gate into the first yard at the bottom of the hill. They walked up a few steps, opened the front door and went in. Never, had I seen them knock or go to the back door. They had been working together each day for the past twenty-five years at the Vanderberg's. The family they worked for must have had a different idea about Negro people. It was the smallest house on the block, freshly painted medium green with dark brown trim, surrounded by flower and vegetable gardens with many fruit trees. Its size did not indicate the need for as much care as the large two-story Ranch Style house I worked in. Based on the delicious smells emanating from the bags Bessie and Bruce carried with them as they boarded the afternoon bus and the beautiful flowers they sometimes had, caused me to imagine their job duties must have included cooking and gardening.

DARLENE'S AWAKENING

The remaining four of us continued going up the hill to our various jobs. The energetic conversations these women shared each morning were usually topics related to the church they all attended. One of those days, they were discussing how God gave his only son to sacrifice his life for our sins. I tried to understand why God would have given his child for the mistakes people made. It made no sense, it was a puzzle to me. Were the many sins Colored people had done much bigger and demanded more attention than those of other races? I knew that as a race we had faults like all others but considering slavery and all of the injustices we had endured it would appear that was enough and would balance out our mistakes. Based on my understanding, Negro people had not castrated, hanged anybody or done many of the other horrible things. If we Coloreds had been in control, would we also have been brutal to others? Are we each individually responsible for the choices we make? Maybe I did not have the right idea or maybe I was not holy enough. The one thing I was certain of was, I knew for sure that I would never have given up a child of mine to be sacrificed for the sins of others. I questioned what might Anthony's comments have been?

In retrospect, it was probably to my advantage not to have been generally included in their discussions because my questions might have weakened their foundations or could have posed ideas these ladies had not wanted to investigate. Listening to their conversations, as we walked slowly up the hill each morning gave me a better understanding of the plight of our Colored people. Judging what these Domestic women discussed, their lives had been dominated by fear and a feeling of low self-worth. Their belief was that Jesus was coming again to save them and all they were required to do was be good as possible and support the church. As I continued walking alone up the hill these thoughts provided more unanswered confusion. Every morning as each of these Domestics went into the various locations where they worked, I was left alone to continue going up the hill the remaining blocks by myself. The thought occurred to me that possibly, the job became available to me, a younger person, because the climb to the top of the hill each day was too strenuous for the others. Generally, I silently probed the discussions I had been privy to and tried to weigh the different opinions. However, before all considerations had concluded, my place of employment had been accessed.

The spring morning most remembered was being in the midst of a hailstorm as we Domestics departed the bus. The strong, blowing winds were causing the hailstones to sting and occasionally hurt my legs. Attempting to open the umbrella to protect my head while going up the hill to avoid the pieces of hard ice falling from the sky in all directions was a one- time experience. Basic survival and preparedness had taught us to always carry the required gear in our bags: an umbrella, flashlight, water, band-aids, matches and a change of clothes. We were all running to escape the danger as quickly as possible. The three other housekeepers were shouting advice for my protection because my job site was the furthest up the hill. Even though I did not share the personal relationship with the other women, we had a silent connection that was evident on this horrible morning as they expressed concern for my safety.

In the four and a half years, I had worked at this location and had ridden the bus with these same employees, in pouring rain, oppressive heat or golf- ball sized hail, never once had I seen or heard of an employer who offered a Domestic a ride up or downhill even when leaving or arriving at the same time. I eased my thoughts with the idea, that perhaps, I was invisible, perhaps all Colored people were invisible. As ludicrous as this might have been, the absurdity of it gave me an unremitting power that had left an indelible memory. I was able to brush aside an attachment to anger by acknowledging my secret invisible power. It provided me an opportunity to have a job and hope when I was as old as the women who exited the bus with me, brighter horizons would be my continual reality. How? When? Where? I did not know, but I somehow believed I would not always have to be invisible. Were there others who shared the feeling of invisibility?

DARLENE'S AWAKENING

Janice and Byron Coode were the couple I worked for. Their home was a typical Ranch style design, larger than most of the others in this area, it had two-stories with two bedrooms and two bathrooms upstairs. A guest bedroom, bathroom, den, office, a dining room, living room, kitchen, laundry room, and a smaller room she referred to as the worker's room were all situated on the lower level. Each day as I arrived, unlike the Masons, the older couple I exited the bus with, who entered into the front door of their workplace was never an option for me. Going through the front door at the Coode's was not even a consideration for a Domestic worker. The back of the house was where my entrance must always be, where all of my belongings must remain, and must never be integrated into any other section of the house.

Most mornings when I arrived, I was exhausted and would have liked to have had a moment or two just to regain my energy. The moment I walked into the house Janice Coode would yell from another room to tell me to check out the day's list of instructions that had been left on the table. She never said good morning. Almost immediately before I could catch my breath, in a very dictatorial manner she told me to change into my uniform and where to begin. At the back of the house into the little worker room reserved for the help, there was a toilet, a sink, a small table and chair where I ate my lunch. For brief moments, the bathroom became an escape place for me to sit and retrieve my breath. "It's time to get started, you are on the clock," she would sometimes shout to me. I didn't suppose Mrs. Coode understood about the tiredness I felt after walking five steep blocks uphill, maybe she just did not care. I was positive she had never trekked up those five blocks. Being thought of as an equal human by this woman seemed to have never entered her consciousness. To me, my invisibility manifested and was more apparent whenever I had to relate to her. This disregard she continually demonstrated prompted me to ask, " Why God, why?" Those were some of the times when I remembered Anthony's words, "we are all alone as a people, no higher power to protect us. We were a mistake in creation." I still could not accept his ideas and I knew for a fact that I was not anyone's mistake, but I did have many unanswered questions.

The daily list placed on the table designated my chores for the day. First, laundry was done, washed, folded and put away, second the kitchen was spotlessly clean, all dishes had to be washed, put on shelves, the floor swept and mopped and then the chores for other areas in the house began, vacuuming, mopping, waxing floors, washing windows, wiping walls, dusting, polishing silver, cleaning crystal, and on and on and on each day. The chores were allocated, depending on her choice of priorities.

I had accepted my life's assignment as a Colored female Domestic with no aspirations of advancing to a more stimulating, more challenging position. There had been no training or any preparation to do anything differently. The job as a Domestic worker was the position I was qualified to fulfill. Those women I walked up and down the hill with each day had accepted their jobs as the only available option for a Negro Female-Domestic at this time. If you were lucky to have your own business, be married to a preacher or maybe a singer in a band were the main employment opportunities that were available. If the skin were lighter, a few other opportunities might be possible but there weren't many options. My job preferences may not have been so limited had I had more skills, typing or some other office work. I chose not to learn a trade after my graduation because money was needed to sustain the two of us and Mama Betty's health had declined. Getting a job as a Domestic was the only option I knew of in 1951 when I was eighteen years old.

DARLENE'S AWAKENING

My Grandmother, Mama Betty was born in 1891, twenty-six years after legal Slavery had officially come to an end. As a child she had worked in the cotton fields, later learned to cook and helped in the kitchens, at one point she was a Wet Nurse, she tended the gardens, cared for animals and was also a midwife. Mama Betty told me the job as a midwife was the one she loved the best, because it gave her the ability to see the sweetness and innocence of a new born first-hand. The majority of the babies she assisted in bringing into the world were White. Sometimes, late at night when the stillness had overtaken the sounds of the crickets a car pulled up to transport her on the other side of the BAILEY to assist in the welcoming of a newborn. I do not think it mattered to her if it were during the bright light of the sun's rays or a shadowless time when all seemed paused, she felt her ability to bring a newborn into this world was a gift, and her role was very important being that she would be the first person the newly arrived would see. Mama shared with me as she looked into their eyes a message of hope prickled her skin as she would very quietly say "I love you," to the fresh little infant. According to her, it was the way in which she might plant a beautiful seed that would eventually produce a kind-hearted, more humane person. She told me she was happy and felt some responsibility whenever there was a request for her services as a midwife. In her almost insignificant way, she was attempting to influence those unsuspecting newborns with a message of love. Looking back and realizing the important role she played as a messenger of hope, I have more and more respect for the person my Grandmother Betty was. The older I have become the more I have gained a deeper realization and appreciation of the amazing examples she demonstrated as a person with limited formal education.

Grandmother Betty had wanted me to go to a trade school or maybe a college, but our lack of finances prevented that. My grandmother was my strongest supporter and had taken such good care of me as I was growing up. Tears welled up in her eyes from time to time as she remembered my father, her son. "You remind me so much of him," she would sometimes repeat. I tried to imagine her sorrow when she received the news of my parent's fatal accident.

My young age and the time lapse since my parent's death had prevented me from remembering specific details of them. The sorrow I experienced as my grandmother's health became weaker and weaker was much more than I was prepared for. Mama Betty was my prop. She had provided my foundation whenever my needs were obvious and times when I had no awareness that I was in want. Sometimes a kiss on the cheek, a soft, powerful, caressing hug or words of encouragement were the tools she offered. The times I needed to be held-up, or more support was required I depended on her. She taught me to believe I could accomplish whatever I chose, and that no person was better than I. She often reminded me to love God, love myself, love others and then everything would forever be okay. Many times, Mama Betty repeated to me the importance of forgiveness and the necessity of being a good person, kind and patient with others and myself. Her wisdom and wise words of advice have given me a power with memories that will be never ending. Kindness, strength and wisdom were some of the tools she gave me. The last words to me from my grandmother as she was dying were,

" You are strong and very smart. You will be just fine." A big smile lit up her face as she passed away. She was a light in my life. Her illumination reminded me that maybe darkness comes, but the light always returns.

PRIVILEGED OVERVIEW

Ironed, steamed, crisp, wrinkle-free attire
Marble, granite faces chiseled to perfection
Polished syntax, perfectly chosen verbs
Boarding- Schools, Equestrian trails
Free-flowing financial streams
Ingesting costly delicacies to the extreme
Sipping martinis from long stemmed proper flukes
Must not be disturbed by petty annoyances
Having all the answers, allowing no questions
Always correct, not politically so
Too important, so important, very important

Fourth Chapter

ILLUSIONS OF SUPERIORITY

My sister Lorna, Grandmother Betty and I usually didn't have extra funds for anything. We lived a simple life, but our home was spotlessly clean.

Working for the Coodes was my first job of earning a regular weekly salary. Monday mornings when I arrived, the kitchen was usually in total disarray with the litter from the weekend; empty bottles, boxes, plates and other garbage strewn about, lying in wait for the Domestic. Who cleaned in my absence? My availability or non-availability had probably never been a consideration. Since the first day I began working for this couple, my attendance had been one hundred percent. It was as if putting dirty dishes into the sink or putting trash into the garbage pail might have been an insult to their social status. It was difficult for me to understand the ways of the Coodes.

There were three restaurants where food was alternatively ordered from each day. Maybe on Mondays the kitchen was a mess because Janice or Byron had decided to cook on the weekend, even though I didn't believe this, it was a solution to my reasoning, explaining as to why there was so much clutter when the two of them usually did not cook or prepare meals.

The refrigerator was mostly empty except for eggs, bacon, some Brie cheese, a product I had never eaten before, usually a container of orange juice, bread and several bottles of wine. A surprise for me was the day I discovered a large piece of cake, fish in a cream sauce, some rice that was other than the usual white color I was familiar with and some peas sitting on one of the shelves. Perhaps, there had been a party and food was brought home. It remained untouched from Monday until Friday when she left additional instructions on her daily note asking me to dispose of it. Such waste was hard for me to accept, because I knew there were so many hungry people who would have appreciated a decent meal. Several times, I had been instructed to throw perfectly good food away, it was never offered to me. Why was there such constant waste?

Monday morning was the day most dreaded for me because usually the kitchen was strewn with containers from the three different restaurants that had been delivered on Friday, Saturday and Sunday. Boxes, paper bags, and a mixture of food containers were on the table, counters and some trash on the floor. This system was unfamiliar to me. If there were no Domestics, would trash pile up, would dirty dishes stack up until a disaster happened? Were those people never trained to pick up after themselves or was there an attitude where they assumed others were obliged to clean up after them.

The "so called Privileged," considered these to be mundane unnecessary obligations that were beneath them. The Housekeepers had the responsibility of handling their garbage, washing their underwear, and cleaning up whatever they dirtied. Did they permit their convoluted judgements to justify some of the reasons a Domestic was able to be treated with such disregard?

DARLENE'S AWAKENING

Janice and Byron Coode's behavior towards each other was not typical of most couples I had known. In the years of working for them, I had never seen them touch or have much conversation with each other. It appeared to be a strange and confusing relationship when I compared it to the relationship I had with my husband. Anthony had to be threatened with the broom in order to force him to leave me alone sometimes. His superstitious nature caused him to be fearful if he were touched with a broom. Somewhere in his past, he had learned that being touched with a broom would bring him bad luck. The broom became my savior when his eagerness took control of his sensibilities. I would hold the broom in front of me and laugh as he turned away.

I wondered what exactly was meant by "bad luck," because the number of complaints he shared would have been an indicator of his life moving in a very unfulfilling direction without being touched with a broom. What responsibility do we have for the unhappiness we encounter? Are there choices we make that can circumvent negativity? Are there beliefs that we subscribe to that help to manifest our life's path?

My observations of the Coodes were puzzling; two married people, who lived together and appeared to disregard each other. How could you marry a person, live in close proximity and ignore each other? Maybe when I was not present, the Coodes had a happy, raucous relationship.

She had closets with mink coats, fancy velvet and silk gowns, lots of jewelry, shoes and purses of every describable color. Hers were garments that might have been displayed in upscale fashion magazines. Based on the quantity of elegant clothes, my assumption was this couple attended numerous important events. In spite of all her possessions, she never seemed very happy.

Mrs. Coode's schedule was predictable, each day at exactly 3:15, I would answer the door, pay the delivery person and place the food into the serving dishes. Wednesdays at 1:15 Janice went to the hair salon to have her hair trimmed and styled. At 3:30 she returned home with a bag of food she had picked up at a restaurant. My duty was to set the table, put the food into serving dishes and set it on the stove. On Fridays, at 2:30 she went to her therapy session. At 4:00, I left and had no idea about their evenings.

Mr. Coode was a tall decent looking man, but definitely not a type I would have chosen. His slightly curly hair was brown and his eyes a greenish color. Did he ever eat? In all the years I had worked at their house, no matter when I arrived or left never had I witnessed this man eating anything. He may have had snacks in his office, I wouldn't have known because that room was off limits to me and I was forbidden to enter it. The first day I began working for the Coodes, Janice told me to never go into his office because he had important papers that must not be bothered. It was of no concern to me because that would have added more work to my schedule. The six and a half hours I worked each day, he was usually very quiet in his office or on extended telephone calls. With this man I was also invisible, something about him felt eerie and strange. Never exchanging the slightest acknowledgement, no apparent visible contact, but several times I observed him staring as if he were peering through me, as if there were a huge hole in my body, as if his eyes were stationery and could not move. I began to suspect that possibly he was near-sighted or far-sighted or a little blind. Whenever he entered a room I was in, immediately I interrupted my chore, exited with the pretext of some other obligation.

These two people would not have been my first choice of employers; however, working for them, in 1951 at 18 years old and earning six dollars a day, plus bus fare was the best and the only job I thought I was able to get as an uneducated, inexperienced young Colored Girl Domestic.

DARLENE'S AWAKENING

PERSPECTIVES

On the third Sunday in May, 1954, while sitting on the sofa after dinner in the living room, some of Anthony's jazz music playing in the background on the record player, absorbing the newly blossoming flower fragrances of spring, listening to the calls of the birds alerting others to the day's curtain closing, succumbing to the embrace of my beloved who had prepared a special feast of pot roast and gravy with mashed potatoes, mustard greens, sliced tomatoes and lemon meringue pie for dessert, feeling as if solutions were just waiting to be invited in, the telephone rang. So surprised when I discovered the caller was Janice Coode. Her behavior and attitude towards me were so uncharacteristic, in fact, I did not know how to respond. The way in which she spoke to me did not represent her usual style, she was polite, gentle, and offered a sense of caring. She was extremely friendly and invited me to arrive at her home earlier the next day. This did not seem to be the woman I had worked for, for almost two years. Janice's call was a definite interruption, intrusion into what had been a nearly perfect evening for Anthony and me. After the call, there was a change in the room, a quiet, uncomfortable, unexplainable uneasiness.

The many obtrusive questions that were overpowering my objectivity took control. Why did she call me? Why was she so friendly? Was I no longer invisible to her? Why did she want me to arrive earlier? Did she have a gift for me? The questions had no limits. As I posed these to my husband who had sat patiently observing me in my confusion, he reminded me again not to have big expectations because the disappointment could be hurtful for me. Anthony repeated several times," I just don't want you to get hurt. That woman has not changed so fast. How was she, what was she like when you last saw her? She was the same! You believe that in two days, she has become different? Wake up, Darlene!" His comments burrowed deeply into my psyche, more of his negative perspectives which I was beginning to lose patience with. My disagreement was that people could change and why couldn't he accept that fact. He did not believe she could have changed so quickly.

Anthony had told me repeatedly how naive I was. Many things would have been done differently had my awareness back then been what it has evolved to now, I supposed others could also say that. As I reflect back, maybe my innocence was coupled with fear and insecurity. Possibly, there was no innocence, only an inability to know who I was or what I wanted. Mama Betty had passed on and it felt as though a wedge was developing and helping to create a distance between my husband and me. There was nothing distinct enough for me to identify, but our relationship had become different.

So many, seemingly unnecessary problems. The increasing numbers of concerns did not provide enough answers. Most of the frustration had been generated by Anthony's unhappiness. Having stable employment gave me a satisfaction that deterred fear of being unable to care for myself. My life has always been relatively simple and protected. I had grown up in this same community, never ventured far and knew most of the residents. The farthest I had ever traveled was to Liston about 100 miles away to meet some of Anthony's family.

DARLENE'S AWAKENING

The pleasurable time, Anthony and I had been sharing prior to the phone call came to an abrupt halt. My curiosity took over my reasoning. Mrs. Coode might have had an unexpected realization that changed her mind and she wanted to show her humanity. Perhaps she had had an epiphany. I was willing to give her the benefit of the doubt. After all, Janice attended her Lutheran Church regularly and volunteered with children. Pictures of Jesus, and many other religious Icons were placed on the walls or on tables in most of the rooms.

It occurred to me at different times when dusting those pictures of Jesus if this could be the same person I had been taught about at church, how could he accept the way in which I was not considered to be an equal human? The color of Jesus in the pictures was of an extremely light skin. Several of them showed Jesus with hair the color of the hay in the pastures. At my church, Jesus did not look exactly the same.

In my Sunday School classes, Jesus' slogan was taught regularly," Do unto others as you would have them do unto you" Did Jesus have special care about my role as a Negro, if not, then why should I await his return? In church there were always references about Jesus coming again. The confusion that entered my mind as I was cleaning caused me to wonder if Jesus came again, would I still have to clean-up for other people.

There were no pictures of the Coode's families posted anywhere in the house, which was strange to me. That night after Janice's call, my sleep was intermittent due to the degree of my agitation. Earlier than usual on Monday morning, I arrived at the bus stop. None of the neighbors who were usually present were visible, even Mrs. Wilson was not in her yard. I wondered what her reaction must have been that morning when she didn't see me. Boarding the bus with a different driver, and unfamiliar passengers we rode along, passing the familiar businesses, many which had not yet opened.

Riding along in silence, sadness overtook me when I remembered the conflict my husband and I had. I loved this man so, very much but his negativity about everything was becoming more than I wanted to deal with. In those earlier years of our marriage bright sparkles tempering future hopes and loving acceptance of each other were a part of our dreams. The almost storybook future we had planned would include the addition of two children. A love and respect for each other that would become stronger and stronger allowing nothing or no one to interfere with our connection. That was our private and very personal commitment we had made to each other. With the acceptance of that agreement, we felt certain our family desires would be complete

The dream of the continuation of our love let me be more patient with my husband. For several years, we had attempted for me to get pregnant, but never, ever did it happen. Finally, after much frustration we both were tested, proving I was fertile and could easily reproduce. The doctors told Anthony he had an extremely low sperm-count and the possibility of him being able to reproduce was very slim. He did not want to share this information with me. Later he told me, he didn't think he was a complete man.

As a teenager, he had worked at a meat packing company. His main job each day was to spray DDT, Malathion or different poisons for rats and or other vermin, never using protective gear, a mask or gloves. Anthony shared about a time after mopping the floor and while wringing out the mop, a horrible rash erupted and covered most of his body. His description of the symptoms about how he itched for several hours and felt like he was losing control of his senses. He scratched so severely that a few permanent scars had remained on his arms and legs. He describes it as the worst experience of his life. The Company doctor gave him a salve and told him it would go away soon. It did not go away and finally his grandmother applied her family potion of clay, pulverized leaves and castor oil to give him relief.

When he returned to his job, and asked for another position, his boss refused, it was his first time to quit a job. A new precedent was begun whereby if he felt he was unjustly treated or with a degree of disrespect, immediately the job was surrendered. I admired his desire for self–respect, even though the challenges were arduous when the need for basic necessities and finances were scarce.

Our family doctor told him the dangers of the poisons he had used as a teenager may have been the catalyst for his low sperm count. Those particular poisons were called Endocrine Disruptors because they interfered with the hormonal systems sexual developmental production. For more than a week, he was silent and refused to touch me.

Some of what had made our relationship special and wonderful were the physical exchanges we shared. From the first moment we connected, there was a link like no other I had ever experienced. A warm safe and loving connection where I felt completely embraced, a sense of security where I felt protected, a nurturing that consoled me when I was vulnerable.
Our intimate times were never about sex, but about making and sharing love. Nothing was present except our connection to each other as we projected ourselves into a state of freedom. The love Anthony and I shared during these intimate moments transported us beyond earthly limitations to vistas the imagination could not fathom. From the first moment we coupled, there was a link like no other I had imagined. A complete embrace, a sense of security where I felt total protection, a nurturing to console me when I was vulnerable, a safe and loving association. In the earlier years of our marriage, we would passionately embrace before leaving for work or wherever we had to go. We were determined that our relationship would be long lasting and no matter the circumstances, our love would be strong enough to bind us. We had decided a very long time ago to say, " I love you," to repeat those words to each other as often as possible.

The fire that occurred when I was five years old had killed both of my parents and had prevented me from having a deep knowing of them. After his parents divorced Anthony realized he had never heard them verbally express their love for each other. Their divorce angered him to the extent that he never forgave them.

Professing our deep commitment to each other as often as possible was a goal we were determined to honor. With those three words, I was assured that all was okay, that all would be okay. When I was burning with passion, welcoming our togetherness, willing to surrender to whatever, to that which made us as one, I discovered that while I was rejoicing from the joy of our relationship, he was having doubts about his ability to feel whole, about his ability as a complete man, about his distrust of a higher Power. This was in such contrast to my happiness with him. Discovering these inconsistencies in my husband's acceptance of himself and his inability to know that together we would be able to overcome any limiting obstacles, created doubts that gave me pause.

Finally, I exited the bus and to my surprise, Janice was waiting in her car and blew the horn for me to come and get in. As I approached her, a big smile emanated from her face, a look I had never been privy to. With this new attitude, she still did not permit me to sit in the front seat next to her and gestured for me to sit in the back seat. The thought of her being my chauffeur would have generated non- stop teasing had the other Domestics I usually walk up the hill with been present that day. My private feelings were laughable. As she drove up the hill, she was talking non-stop about the surprise that was awaiting us. Each time I began to speak she continued as if she did not hear me, I was not permitted to talk. The only choice given to me was to relent. I was not her equal and we were not permitted to participate as equals in casual conversation. Being aware of my invisible self in her presence reminded me to have no reaction, but to realize her limitations in spite of her attempt to be friendlier.

As Lorna and I were growing up there was much advice from Mama Betty. A particular suggestion was to be aware of the un-spoken behavior of others during conversation, be aware if there is an equal exchange, and become a good listener. For a person with almost no formal education, I realize more and more Mama's degree of wisdom.

DARLENE'S AWAKENING

The relationship or non-relationship with my employer provided continuous lessons. At work our relationship was that typical model of an employer and employee with confused definitions of superiority and inferiority. I had no investment in Janice Coode except because of her, I had a job. Listening to her and not being allowed to even ask a question could have been interpreted as rejection. After several of my attempts to verbalize were dismissed, I chose to smile and not give her dialogue much credence.

The questions I had wanted to ask were not that important to me. As I reflect back, I realize that my role was to listen and not speak. I rode in the car with her, but it was if I didn't exist, as if I were invisible. The more she talked about her surprise, the degree of my curiosity had taken flight and ventured into faraway realms. Once we arrived at the house, she entered through the front door and even though she was exhibiting a change in her behavior, the Colored Domestic was still invisible when it came to going into her home through the front door as she gestured for me to go to the back entrance. I entered the worker room and changed into my uniform as I listened to her excitement while calling for me to hurry and come into the living room.

My imagination was soaring and had overtaken me as I hurried to change my clothes. My foolish imagination was running rampant. Rushing into the living room, I was halted by the contrast of what had been and what was now. The color pink had replaced the monochromatic tan tones. The expression generated on my face would have caused a saner person to question my emotions. She was so involved in her intention, that her unawareness of me was not significant. This woman had no idea as to who I was or that I might have value. It was at that moment I became aware that Janice Coode, my employer was much more complicated than I had realized. What was her husband's attitude? Were they both in a state of a discordant illusion? How could anyone with the amount of money they must have had decorate a room to look this way? Did she consult a home decorator? Did this home transformation represent the décor of the homes of her friends? The years I had been her employee, never had a friend visited.

The one friend she mentioned from time to time was Beth Ann, a woman who attended her church. One of the most memorable occasions for me was on the day Beth called as Mrs. Coode was beginning to make an apple pie. She rolled out the crust, put it into the pan, sliced apples then added them along with spices, sugar, lemon juice and butter, covered the ingredients with an upper crust and placed them into the oven. She and her only friend were still engaged in conversation as the pie baked forty-five minutes. After the pie was removed from the oven and allowed to cool, she cut a slice, ate it and the two women were still talking and seemingly, still very dedicated to their phone conversation. During this entire time, I was allowed to have first-hand observation while standing at the kitchen counter polishing silver, overhearing their discussion and appreciating the succulent aroma of the apple pie. I assumed their conversation was of a very serious nature when Mrs Coode replied," My grandaddy gave me a small ivory-handled pistol and told me it was for my protection. He said with all these Coloreds running around, especially the males. it was good to be prepared to protect ourselves. I keep it close to me just in case, you never know." Her words did not surprise me. The aroma of the pie had minimized their conversation and the golden-brown crust once it was removed from the oven had a sensory appeal.

Just out of respect, I had assumed because I was working next to her during the making of the pastry, she might have offered me a slice; however, I had no expectations from this woman whose continual attitude whenever she related to me was as if I were not a part of the human species. A prepared, baked and consumed pie with a non-stop phone conversation was a first time I had seen or heard such behavior. It was not a complete surprise when no piece was offered. Such a polite gesture might have shocked me to a point where portions of my underpinnings could have crumbled.

DARLENE'S AWAKENING

Continuously I had to remind myself that her awareness of me and other Negroes is one of fear and ignorance. The teachings and acceptance of racism have given ignorant descendants a false sense of superiority. Slavery and its fallout have left an impenetrable legacy. The status in which she resided does not require apologies, respect or any degree consideration. Janice Coode and others of her ilk subscribed to a conscious acceptance that some groups of people are not required to have an equal position in society therefore giving permission for justifiable maltreatment of others.

Her insistence that I walk around and look closely at the changes she had been responsible for was indeed mystifying. Janice was smiling and appeared extremely pleased to share her latest accomplishment with me.

The living room had been transformed from a previously boring, nondescript, room where the sofa, chairs, rugs and curtains were all of the same tan and white hue with darker brown accents. Previously, it had reminded me of the room at the mortuary where Mama Betty's body was laid when I attended her Wake. The sadness generated whenever I was in the living room was unexplainable; therefore, rushing to complete chores and exit quickly were primary concerns when cleaning that room. It was adjacent to Mr. Coode's office, an additional impetus to depart the particular location as fast as possible.

Entering this room, the fresh smell of paint was overwhelming. The new pink color was everywhere, covering everything, not a subtle pink as my maid's uniform, but bright. It was reminiscent of the time when as a child, I had drunk some of Grandmother Betty's bright pink, good tasting medicine. For many hours after the initial ingestion, I vomited, endured horrible stomach pains, sweat ran down my brow, dizziness prevented me from standing, and there was this pink smelly, awful substance all over my clothes. For some unknown reason, Mama Betty did not appear to be very concerned. She smiled and told me it was not poison and I was having a good cleansing. As a seven-year-old child, I did not know exactly what she meant, but the pink colored medicine etched an unforgettable scar

---

70

The floors were covered with a bright pink shag carpet. A pink satin French Provincial sofa with carved legs and three matching chairs were placed in a semicircle in front of the big bay window. Above the sofa was an oversized pink, crystal chandelier. The coffee tables and two smaller tables followed the color theme and were also supported by carved pink legs. Little ornate ceramic figurines sat on each table. Above the fireplace was a huge oval mirror surrounded with porcelain pink flowers and touches of green leaves. Porcelain pink figurines, angels, ballerina dancers and fairies accented with gold or pink were placed on the mantle. On one of the walls, there were paintings of pink flowers with gold frames. Opposite these, a singular, huge pink rose filled the space. Pink lamps displayed with coils of filigree snakes from the base to the top of the lamp and transparent silk pink shades. Janice explained these were the latest French designs in home furnishings. She was talking non-stop and appeared to be happier than I had ever witnessed. It was as if the exuberance regarding this new room design was propelling her to points beyond the imagination. Seeing her smile was a first- time occurrence for me. Seeing her attempt to have a conversation with me instead of following me around criticizing my work was also a first. In actuality, it was not a conversation because she did all of the talking and when I made an attempt to comment, she interrupted. I followed my usual pattern of listening to her and smiling when I could, just to make her think whatever she was sharing mattered.

Was this woman so divorced from reality or so self-absorbed that she had no understanding about how this would affect me? Did she believe I would be happy with her living room transformation? Janice Coode, had called me the night before, interrupted a perfectly special time for my beloved and me. More effort and patience I had been giving to our marriage because the collective closeness Anthony and I had shared was slowly degenerating.

DARLENE'S AWAKENING

I became embarrassed because of my expectations from this woman. As I reflect back, possibly I had an unaware need for her acceptance of me which was deeper than I realized. I had allowed my imagination to interrupt my reasoning. My husband had warned me, but because of his critical approach to so many things, I ignored him. She had picked me up from the bus stop and driven me up the hill to the house. Why? It was puzzling, perplexing and confusing as to how Janice viewed me. I assumed her opinions of me did not have much consideration. When she directed me to enter from the back of her house as she entered through the front door, my invisibility to her was even more obvious.

What do you think, isn't this incredible? Everybody knows that you people, you Coloreds really like colors, so I assumed you would think it was special and I wanted to share something nice, I thought we both would enjoy it. What do you think?" I had allowed the comment "you people," with its bitter implication, to enter my consciousness, pierce my sensibilities, penetrate my insecurity, puncture my verbal ability and agitate my mental frustration. My thoughts slowly calmed down, when I was reminded of my Grandmother and remembered my impermanent and vulnerable position as a Domestic. Breathing in slowly and deeply, I recalled the fear and ignorance Janice exemplified. "What do you think?" she repeated.

Eyeballing this transformed room reminded me of the annual circus that came to our community in celebration of Juneteenth. It was similar to the Fun House I once visited with bells and dangling trinkets. The only missing element was the sound of an organ grinder with a little dancing monkey, wearing a hat soliciting donations from the onlookers

It was an embarrassing moment for me, but I knew I must remain in integrity with myself, after taking a deep breath, my response was, "Oh my goodness! You did this, it is amazing!? Oh, my goodness this is truly amazing. When I left on Friday, the room had not changed. You must have worked all weekend. This is amazing."

The entire time I was speaking, she was smiling. Several years of working as her Domestic, this was the first time I had seen her smile. The attempt she had made to share something special with a Colored person must have been a confusing victory. "Well, I had a little help from some of my church youngsters. The teenagers did all of the painting on Friday evening. On Saturday, kids from the youth group came to assist with the final touches. The younger children carefully unpacked the boxes of figurines. It was a big celebration. The Cottage Restaurant prepared the food: hot dogs, peanut butter and jelly sandwiches, potato salad, ice cream, juice, fresh apples, celery sticks and fried chicken. It was a feast and the nicest weekend I have had in a long time. When I told the children, a Colored girl was my maid, some of them told me how Coloreds really like bright colors and that I should surprise you. My therapist had suggested I do something nice for a person I was not close to, so I figured it would make you happy, and also please my therapist."

"Well, this is truly amazing." I repeated again. She appeared to be satisfied with my response. Responding in this manner, Anthony might not have understood, but it made her feel good and my responsibility to myself remained in integrity. Being diplomatic and holding onto my job was a priority. Grandmother Betty reminded me as I was growing up , there would be times when it became necessary to listen to the opinions of others, agreeing with them was not a necessary condition, but a smart person finds a way not to be confrontational, or express dissatisfaction, especially with one's employer.

DARLENE'S AWAKENING

Anthony did just the opposite if he did not agree with another person, whether it was his boss or anyone, he always expressed his opinion. He once told me not to be a "kisser upper." There are those times when, "biting one's tongue," and listening can be the best option. Having been fired multiple times was an indicator of the necessity for him to just breathe in and be quiet. Had we been able to reproduce and have children, would his attitude have been different? Would he have thought of himself as a complete man? With his uncertain employment, I recognized that I must have a means to support myself. My employment as a Domestic worker was the only option I was aware of. In addition to my repulsion of the pink, the idea that I was going to have to clean this conglomeration and spend more time in an area of the house I attempted to avoid was not a hospitable thought. The non-descript tan room from the past offered a more pleasant contrast.

According to Janice, she had followed the suggestion of her therapist by doing something nice and sharing the good sentiments with another person who might not be as privileged as she was. Apparently, my employer had never related to a Negro person as an equal and was attempting to reach out in her limited way. Her limitations were not surprising to me. I had lived in this racially divided town from the day of my birth. The racial divisions that were evident as one crossed the BAILEY had been an accepted part of our culture.

Travel adventures away from my well-known community were more than limited, they had been non-existent. Reading various publications with pictures of mysterious faraway places had lit a flame in my curiosity. Somehow, I sensed that my ordinary existence, my daily acceptance of what was supposed to be normal would vanish and more opportunities would burst forth. It was a feeling I had imagined for many years. Since I was a little girl, I had been aware that for me or people who looked like me certain opportunities were not available.

Many years of hearing family and friends share about their employer's neurotic behaviors had paved the way for me not to be reactive. Her attempt to reach out in a more humane way was awkward, but as we approached the house, and she went to the front door, and pointed for me, Mrs. Invisible to go to my usual back entrance, I was reminded that no major changes had occurred, possibly temporary ideas in her mind that gave her an ability to feel better about herself.

It was not a part of my job description to question her weekly appointments to counseling sessions. She mentioned her therapist which to me as a Colored was not what we did in our community. First of all it took more money than most of us had. To be a Negro might attract unwelcomed racism, pity and other negatives. To be thought of as "crazy, someone with a screw loose, or just a damn fool" was definitely not an acceptable or attractive tag. In our Colored area there were other options, if your religion allowed, you were able to shout or scream in Sunday Service. Catholics went to confession, others talked to someone they felt could be trusted, alcohol was a tool that gave a temporary escape, and a small number ended their lives. These were the primary options for residents who lived east of the BAILEY when life's demands opened up infections oozing with poison where no solutions resided.

In fact, as a relatively invisible employee, it was none of my business to know if it were a psychologist, psychiatrist, a witch-doctor, maybe her minister or some other counselor who was giving her guidance. It became very apparent after seeing her Pink Living Room that I was working for a person whose "elevator did not go to the top floor." That was an expression I heard Anthony use when he referred to some of his bosses. Whatever the expression meant, I was happy she was in the care of what I hoped was someone who knew how to help. Most Domestics shared that their female employers attended weekly therapy sessions to get help of some kind. My assumption was it required for people with a certain amount of money and a particular skin color.

DARLENE'S AWAKENING

My recollection of past Monday mornings when the kitchen was reminiscent of a train wreck offered a welcomed and unexpected vision as I entered. The kitchen had been left clean and orderly. Also, on this particular day, instead of the regular six- hour occupation time, she released me after having worked only four hours and paid me the same six dollars. Would her transformation be long lasting? She was exuberant and when I was preparing to leave, she yelled to me, "We really had a good day, don't you think?" I looked at her and smiled.

Fifth Chapter

SECRETS

As I arrived home, Anthony was waiting to learn about my day. It was difficult to explain because I became very aware of the criticism he was waiting to direct. Sharing with him about her happiness and the indications that she was a troubled person received no empathy from him. He turned, walked away and said dinner would be ready in twenty minutes. The coldness and the unfriendliness he exhibited were not reasonable and all attempts for discussion were pushed away. He put on a clean shirt and left. I was asleep when he returned. The next morning, I prepared breakfast, sat alone silently, ate a piece of toast with peach preserves and drank a cup of coffee. He remained in bed without mumbling a sound as I prepared to leave. Why had his attitude with me become so different? My availability to my husband had always been a priority. Nothing I had done justified his distancing himself from me? A crying heart, a heavy head feeling like it weighed a ton were holding me down.

Walking along the sidewalk to the corner to catch the eight o' five bus the usual neighbors were manning their porches. As I arrived at the bus stop, Mrs. Watson yelled from across the street to inquire what had happened to me the day before? Just as I had gained enough of myself to answer, the bus arrived. The same usual, daily characters that were absent on yesterday's earlier bus were exhibiting their typical behaviors. It could have been a comfortable, familiar journey where I might have relaxed but the moment my eyes closed, an image of Anthony and his rejection overshadowed my relaxation. The rattling sounds and jolting of the bus while crossing the BAILEY alerted my senses and immediately my eyes opened. I had not been aware of Angel Harp, but there she was doing her customary proselytizing.

On this day, she was wearing a purple skirt that had a bright red embroidered waistband, a yellow blouse and a light green scarf. Angel's choice of colors was a bit strong, even for me, a Colored person. I laughed to myself as I remembered Janice and the youngsters from her church referring to how "Coloreds liked bright colors." Possibly some of them had seen Angel on one of those days when her choices of colors electrified one's vision and assigned her the role as the representative for Negroes.

At my exit as we Domestics began ascending the hill, the others had questions as to my whereabouts the previous For several months, my daily routine was always the same, there were no special changes at my job, The Pink Room existed like a protected island that was off limits to the residents. It never appeared to have been used. There was no evidence of anyone having sat on the sofa or of any of the objects having ever been touched. There were never footprints on the shag rug. This room had become more of an outer limit sanctuary. The curtains were never opened and if any amount of light came through, a very bizarre strangeness was revealed.

Mr. Coode could be heard talking on the phone, if the door was ajar; tablets, reams of paper, office materials and paraphernalia on other tables and on the floor could be seen. Perhaps had he had a secretary, there might have been more order. Based on what could be seen when his door was opened, his was a system I unfamiliar with. The little snippets of Mr. Coode's conversations I was able to hear never made sense to me. He would sometimes mention stocks and other terms that were totally unfamiliar. Most days, Janice Coode would polish her fingernails, do crossword puzzles or sit and listen to her favorite soap operas: Stella Dallas, The Guiding Light or a Brighter Day. I had been instructed to never interrupt her when she was listening to those programs on the radio. Many home decorator books and magazines lined the shelves, but I had never seen her read them. Bibles of every size and description had their own particular bookcase.

DARLENE'S AWAKENING

For several months, there were no special changes at work except the day Janice informed me of a new schedule, which precluded her being present when I was there. She told me she trusted me to take good care of her home and was confident I could complete my daily assignments. She would be away from home doing very important work. The once per week therapy session she had grown accustomed to had been increased to an hour and a half three times each week on Mondays, Wednesdays and Fridays. In addition, she had enrolled in an exercise class and a cooking class at the YWCA and other times, she did volunteer work for senior citizens at the Daughters of the American Revolution Center. Her schedule would take up most of her daily hours, but she would continue to leave a work assignment and my pay each day. She reminded me to never bother Mr. Coode because he was extremely busy and needed total autonomy.

I breathed in a very private, secretive sigh of relief. What a break her new plan gave me. For me, it was if I were being released from prison where a new freedom had emerged. An unprecedented change offering me liberation and a promise of more happiness.
day. Without going into much detail, I shared that I had to report an hour earlier. That seemed to relieve their prying.

At home that evening, I shared my delight of this new arrangement with my husband whose attitude was still a bit distant and distrustful. His pattern had also changed. Each evening after dinner, he washed the dishes, put them away, changed clothes and left. His somewhat questionable response to my inquiry was that he was hanging out with his friends. Up to that time, I had no reason not to trust him. The notion did arise as to what he and his buddies could have been doing every night. The idea that his times with his cronies had taken priority over our closeness gave me serious concern. For the past several months, our lovemaking had come to a complete halt. No longer did we play, no more did I have to use the broom as a lighthearted defense. Anthony returned home each evening while I was sleeping.

The next day when I arrived at work Janice had already left. I took my time to change into the uniform and gave myself a moment to catch my breath after having walked up the steep hill. Janice's typical call reminding me that I was on the clock was absent. It was when I sat, regained my sense of self, took my time to change into the uniform that I realized the amount of tension and anxiety I had been under each morning. I supposed after having worked for this couple for almost five years, Janice Coode thought she could have a degree of trust about me.

The day's instructions clean all windows, and the Venetian blinds. were written on a piece of paper laid on the table next to the day's six dollar pay, plus a dollar for bus fare. The note reminded me that Mr. Coode was not to be disturbed. This new arrangement was more pleasing. Usually, if she were not doing her crosswords, she would follow me from room to room. After I had cleaned, her pattern was to double check and redo things I had already done. At first, I was bothered but finally I just ignored her and went to the next task. As the dishes were washed Janice would pick up each one individually, hold it up to the light and inspect it. Having chosen to ignore her insults allowed me to gain more of a sense of myself. After a time, I did not care about the way she would utter a sound with her teeth and tongue after the inspection. I assumed it was a way she demonstrated her power. Today, the first day of my new independence, I cleaned slowly, feeling no stress and completed the day without seeing Mr. Coode. He could be heard talking on the phone and not once did he make an appearance. I was very happy to have had such a relaxing, peaceful time as my workday ended.

The usual Domestics and I walked down the hill to the bus stop. I realized how exhausted I was and the reason we probably did not talk much with each other was because of our physical demands as housekeepers and the multitude of responsibilities we had to take care of each day.

DARLENE'S AWAKENING

Arriving home, Anthony had prepared a most delicious meal, cornbread, collard greens, meatloaf, sweet potatoes and sliced tomatoes. The dinner was great. I was happy and my husband was extremely quiet until he finally revealed that he had been fired again. I attempted to console him, reminding him of his many talents. I even suggested that his cooking was good enough for us to consider opening a small café. We had discussed the idea several times, but Anthony couldn't fully embrace it. His culinary contributions were amazing and so delicious, I was sure if he were the chef, a business based on home-cooked meals would have been successful. I reminded him of the fact that he was able to repair anything that was broken, i.e. small appliances, his car, he painted our house and our neighbor's, or maybe he could take a few classes at night school, but my efforts were in vain. All of my suggestions were rejected, and every plan I proposed, offered no appreciation of the slightest interest.

Anthony slowly walked away and his repeated utterance," I ain't a complete man." I loved this man and in spite of the fact that we would not have our own biological children together, he was still my hero and I just wanted to return to our previous times. What determines whether a person is complete or not? Who makes that determination? Are some of us so lost in our private pain, so hurt by rejection that there is an unawareness of the special qualities each of us has? Are we so controlled by our egos that we need the approval or acceptance of others to recognize our own importance? I had no answers, but I knew there must be something better than acquiescing to the judgements and definitions we give others permission to label us with.

Anthony and his family had lived in Liston, a small rural town about one hundred miles south of this town of Westbrite. His parents were a typical 1950s working- class, Colored family who were attempting to have the basics for themselves and their four children. He was the youngest and only male with three older sisters. Most of the families in his rural town, worked as pickers in the fields. The residents and workers represented multiple ethnicities: Orientals, Mexicans, Negroes and poorer Whites. As a young boy, Anthony resented the fact that he had to work in the fields. As a teenager, he had worked in the small grocery store his parents owned. Stocking shelves, cashiering, and being polite to people whom he did not respect had absolutely no appeal and did not satisfy his yearnings. Into his fourth year as a teenager, his mother and father divorced at a time when he was searching for reasons that made more sense. The divorce severely angered him. He questioned why after so many years of marriage, living together, having four children, attending church each Sunday and being recognized as one of the families to hold in high regard they couldn't work out their differences. When his parents dissolved their relationship, he did not have much trust in anything, or anyone anymore. To Anthony, people were phonies, hypocrites and big liars, especially his parents. In order to distance himself from his family, he got a job in a meat processing company in order not to spend so much time with his family. The harsh judgments he released when he spoke about his mother and father, and his inability to forgive them made me very uncomfortable. The memories I had of my mother and father were so vague. How I would have loved to have had my parents in my life as I was growing up. Are we as a species ever totally satisfied? Anthony had moved away hoping a larger town might offer more peace and a greater distance from his relatives.

From our first meeting, it was as if we were magnetically connected, as sparks burst forth, igniting an unending flame brightening the direction for a lasting happiness.

DARLENE'S AWAKENING

The anger, impatience and other limitations he had chosen to accept prevented him in his forward movement. So desperate was I to return to that relationship we had four years ago when we first met. I no longer knew how to connect with Anthony. The idea of my husband not being a complete man was never a serious consideration for me. From my perspective, Anthony was undamaged whether he was able to reproduce or not. His low sperm count and inability to impregnate me were not the factors that determined my love for him. From the moment we met, he was my Prince. Was he perfect, no? Was I perfect, no? Why the conflict, was the closeness we had shared too frightening for him because of his inability to trust? Why didn't he accept my love and not allow his own limited judgment of himself to interfere with what had been a beautiful relationship? Anthony changed his clothes, went out the door and returned when I was asleep. Each evening when he left, I turned on the radio and went to sleep listening to music as a distraction from the sadness I had begun to have.

I taped a note to the bathroom mirror with hearts and flowers I had drawn and words that were repeated several times," I love you. I love you. I love you, I love you very much. Why can't you love me back? Why won't you love me back?" The next morning when I went into the bathroom, the note was still in its original place attached to the mirror. Of all the people he had discarded, why would he reject me? My love and care for him was genuine. I now wonder if our having had a child together would have guaranteed happiness. Thinking about his parents who had been married over twenty-five years did not assure the happiness in their marriage. All around us there were plenty of people who had had children and unhappy relationships. Many of the people who attended my church regularly were divorced. He didn't realize that to be able to impregnate me was not the main factor in determining if he qualified to be whole.

Many men have children, is that what determines whether they are complete or not? Based on the growing number of men who walk away from their families, it seemed to me that being whole was not an easy decision for men who had been beaten down by a racist society: being whole may have been invalidated by some mothers who scapegoated their male children with corporal punishment that was border line abusive; being whole could not be determined by religion that had not answered their basic questions, by confusion with no solutions, realizing no matter what the condition of the economic status, he would always be a second-class citizen unless he were able to embrace his true self.

When Anthony had such sadness and shared his distrust of so many people and circumstances, I remember thinking, I am happy, I am a female. It is true, that as Colored people, men and women have endured some of the same concerns, but generally our treatment was not as severe as Negro males. Being introduced to the Growth Room and utilizing it and having matured more, I came to the realization that we, ourselves determine if we are Whole. The circumstances do not matter, it is our connection to ourselves. I examined the idea that maybe Anthony would always be reaching to become Whole. If he does not acknowledge the necessity of embracing his talented, beautiful, true self, he might remain in a state of victimization and unhappiness.

Week after week I went to work with a new attitude and a welcome escape from my husband who seemed to be descending deeper and deeper into a state of darkness, who seemed to be moving further and further away from me. I awaited a response from my note, but none was forthcoming.

DARLENE'S AWAKENING

At my job, a new independence emerged that had never been available. With Mrs. Coode's absence and Mr. Coode's lack of interaction, I cleaned, played soft music on the radio, ate my lunch at the kitchen table in total relaxation each day. The bathrooms which had previously been unavailable for my personal use, upstairs and the one downstairs were at my disposal when I chose. These were my very private secrets. What would the boss lady have done had she returned home and witnessed me sitting at her table using her utensils? How would she have reacted had she known I stopped my work and used her bathroom and not the one in the small, windowless room she called the worker's room?

UNFORESEEN CIRCUMSTANCES

It was on a particular day as I was listening to the radio while cleaning the downstairs guest bedroom and just about to complete the day's assignment, when I sensed someone in the room and turned around to see Byron Coode standing in the doorway looking at me. It was that creepy, unsettling stare he had, that caused me to shiver. Before I could inquire as to his wishes, he rushed towards me and forced me down on the bed.

The surprise, horror and fear overpowered and prevented me from the ability to gain control of myself. Before I was able to really get my words out, he had my dress up and over my head. "No, no, Mr. Coode no, no, what is the matter with you? He responded, "be quiet, be quiet. It's okay." I was attempting to scream while one of his hands was frantically tearing off my panties, the other hand was covering my mouth to quell the screams. This man who had never spoken to me, never acknowledged me was lying on top of me inserting his penis into my vagina. I cried, squirmed to get from under his control, but his physical power was too much for me. I cried, and cried as he performed his selfish, oppressive, disrespectful, horrible, sexual act. After he had finished and satisfied his cravings, he got up, didn't look at me and went into the bathroom. I heard water running in the sink. Once finished he went outside, got in his car and drove away. I lay there in such disbelief while attempting to gather myself, there were no words to describe my sorrow. My shock, my surprise, my anger, my hatred of this despicable man who had just taken advantage of me, who had always treated me as invisible had pounced on me and prevented me from moving.

As I slowly got myself together, I remembered my Mama Betty and cried as I wondered what she would have done. Had she ever had to endure such physical abuse, such aggression? I needed someone to talk with. Who would I trust enough and feel safe enough with to share this ugly experience? It definitely could not be my husband. The thought occurred to me, if I told him, would he attempt something foolish to defend my honor? Deep down, I knew he wouldn't, I knew he couldn't. A Negro man who had just been laid off again, a Negro man aware of the possible life-threatening dangers he would face in attempting to defend his wife, a Negro man in search of stability, in search of a happier existence, a Negro man tip toeing on the fringes looking for a permanent security, a Negro man holding on to fear, anger and sadness, A Negro man never feeling whole, a Negro man lost in confusion accepting the legacy of slavery while searching for his purpose, searching for himself. I knew I couldn't share the experience with him, but I needed someone.

DARLENE'S AWAKENING

Lorna, my sister was the only person with whom I felt I could trust; however, not a hundred percent, she talked too much, she was kind and her love for me was obvious, but she was a gossip. Other times, I had thought about the possibility of her and Daisy Crocker writing a book together about the past, present and future of the daily dramas that are unique in our community. I knew my sister loved me undeniably and would be concerned. I really needed someone to talk with. The embarrassment and the shame I felt did not make sense, I was aware that I had not initiated the offense, but still I felt ashamed. Considering the seriousness of the abuse I hoped Lorna would respect my feelings and respect my desire for privacy.

With frantic determination, I began rushing to get away from that house, I went into the worker room to change my clothes and there on the table next to my daily $7.00 was a ten- dollar bill.

Was that my pay for his sexual abuse, for his sexual release, for his overpowering me? Did he feel that by paying me, his abuse was justified? If I took the ten dollars, was I accepting his behavior? Would I be a prostitute or a whore or maybe a call girl? I did not know the difference. His wife paid six dollars plus my bus fare for eight hours per day and he paid ten dollars for twenty minutes.

Anthony was unemployed again. What were the answers? Who was I? My confused reasoning propelled me to put the money into my purse and get away from that place as fast as I was able to.

Going down the hill, almost running, my body behaved as if it were guided by a force beyond recognition. There was no memory of my feet connecting to the ground. I arrived thirty minutes earlier than the usual time. Fortunately, the other familiar Domestics hadn't left their workplaces yet. At the bus stop I was grateful for the alone time and a minute to think. I felt dirty, angry, sad and so, so alone. Entering the bus, locating a seat, closing my eyes and opening them again at my exit was a faraway memory. My recollection of events after the abuse were shrouded in disbelief.

Had this man entertained these thoughts and ideas about me for a long time? Hidden in the recesses of my subconscious mind was I somewhat aware of what his innermost thoughts regarding me were percolating? Did that explain the reason I felt so uncomfortable in his presence?

I vaguely remember exiting the bus and walking from the bus stop passing my neighbors who were sitting on their porches. Whether or not there were mutual acknowledgements, the memories of such have faded.

Entering the house, discovering that Anthony was not there, relieved and allowed me to take a deep cleansing bath and shower.

Lorna came, she informed me that she would not be able to stay very long and had only a few minutes. That was her usual, repeated greeting. I shared my horrible day's experience and she sat down. Tears welled up in her eyes. Lorna's very strong reactions shocked me. The empathy she displayed was so strong, I was concerned to know if it was on my account or was there some other reason? As I continued to tell her about my day, she reluctantly told me of the abuse she had involuntarily endured many times before her boss became ill. Our stories were very related, the female employer would be away from home each day and the boss man took advantage of Lorna for several years.

Many times, I had looked at her youngest two children and decided the lightness of my niece and nephew's skin must have been due to some DNA abnormality. After Lorna shared various elements of her own abuse, questions that had been plaguing me about the two young ones had become clearer.

DARLENE'S AWAKENING

She also told me about three of our church members who had had the same problem with their bosses. According to what she told me, these men had ideas that Colored women were mysterious and great sex partners. She said that most of the female Domestics she knew had been violated. I wondered if that had applied to our Grandmother. My sister told me, my employer would come after me many more times, which he did. It was always the same approach. He would quietly grab me from the rear then turn me around to face him and begin undressing me. I would struggle and ask him not to, even though I knew my words were meaningless. For a long time, many months these encounters persisted. The relationship had become so frequent and so familiar that I gradually relaxed. As much as I relaxed, I didn't accept this abuse, I just lay there keeping my eyes closed. No emotions were emitted, no sounds, no embrace, always I lay quiet and motionless with my arms next to my body. My non-reaction appeared not to matter; I had become a repository for his sperm to be deposited. I realized to him I must have appeared as an invisible, soulless person, without a heart or just an object for him to release his pent- up hostility, cowardice, bullying and disrespect. Was I being honest when I blamed it all on him? What might have happened had I refused more forcefully?

Anthony had become more and more distant, was that a justification for my unconscious acceptance of my boss' abuse? Rarely did my husband prepare meals anymore. His evening whereabouts were puzzling to me and those times when I questioned him, a clear answer was never forthcoming. The love note I had left for him on the mirror several months ago was never given a reply.

I prayed for solutions, but there were no simple answers. Each time I lay under the weight of Mr. Coode's body, my confusion produced hatred, shame, guilt and disgust with myself. Each time he overpowered me, there was a reluctant surrender, but nonetheless a surrender. My attitude was one of constant resentment and never an expression of acceptance. He did not seem to care, in fact it was as though I were not present, only my body. I have no idea if he looked at me because always my eyes were closed. Byron Coode who forced me to lie down with him at least three times a week, I was not familiar with his face.

When my husband and I were in the throes of our ecstatic love-making, I kissed and caressed his face, eyes, ears, lips. Every little scar, or any of the particular identifying marks on Anthony's face were all familiar to me.

Three times a week and sometimes more, the abuse was succumbed to. Is it fair for me to continually call it abuse? The payment was many times more than what I earned as a Domestic. In the beginning when Byron first accosted me, he would leave ten dollars. After a short time with each encounter, a twenty-dollar bill was left on the table. I was now earning almost a hundred dollars a week. Was I accepting his actions because I was being paid? Earning much more than anyone I had known.

Perhaps other Domestics also had secret hiding places where their clandestine salary was hidden. I had begun to think about Lorna's words referencing Domestics sexual abuse and considered maybe that was the reason so many of them held their heads down and didn't look directly into the eyes of another person when they were talking. Was that the reason so many constantly read their bibles? Were the bibles what offered another kind of hope? Was going to work each day and being molested an acceptable, guilt-ridden part of their job description? Many of the Domestics shared how their female bosses were usually not at home because of the various civic duties and the volunteer work that occupied their busy schedules. Never would I have realized there was so much intrigue, guilt, despair and anger as the Domestics, Colored women, Negro women, invisible Ones were attempting to hold on to a job to help keep their families together. Could this be a reason so many Colored women filled the churches each Sunday as a way to assuage some of the shame that had become an extended part of their job description?

DARLENE'S AWAKENING

Not knowing when or where an encounter would take place was a shocker. His strange manner and creepy silence reminded me of an unfeeling disembodied entity I had seen in a movie. The freedom that had sprung forth when Janice Coode began her new schedule was short-lived. Each sound I heard prompted me to constantly look over my shoulders as I was working because Mr. Coode would silently appear and be upon me before I had time to react. As a result, doing my job had become an extremely stressful undertaking.

He accosted me in the bedroom as I was making the beds, on the new pink satin sofa with pink angels and ballerinas watching us, on the floor as they were being polished, in the small, worker, employee's room. He had begun to kiss my lips, and my neck. The day he actually kissed me all over my body I heard him faintly say, "I love you." This quiet phrase made me open my eyes to see him staring at me with that glassy, creepy look that for the past four and a half years had forced me to keep a distance from him. He smiled, and my eyes shut tighter. In that instance, I better understood what his strange subtext must have been all those times I caught him looking at me. I realized why I felt uncomfortable in his presence. This cowardly man had been holding on to his lascivious thoughts until finally, he was able to physically manifest them. Lorna had told me that most of the Domestics were abused in this way.

I wondered if Byron Coode discussed his activities with his associates. Was it an acceptable secret among his White male friends? Did they laugh together and remind each other, that having sex with a Colored Domestic could be fun and a good way to release tension and it was not a thing to be so concerned about, just don't allow them to have babies. The thoughts that overtook my reasoning helped to make me more repulsed by this man.

Lying there while he was satisfying himself, I explored the possibilities of him suggesting, urging and insisting that his wife find "satisfying activities," outside their home each day. Feeling very supported in knowing that her church going husband, a leader in his community was attempting to guide her in a direction that would offer her more fulfillment. What a noble gesture, what an understanding and a supportive husband she must have thought!

A few days later as I was completing my final chore, he appeared. I had thought perhaps because of the lateness of the day I would not be bothered; however, the same exact procedure, he undressed me without conversation and laid me down. His handling of me was gentle, but so powerful my struggle offered no relief. Conversation between us did not exist, I told him I was pregnant, he did not react. I wondered if he had understood me. Byron Coode finished the assault, left the room and quickly returned with two hundred dollars, and told me, "fix the situation immediately and return to work at the end of next week." There was no emotion in his voice, only a direct command as he lay the money down and left the room without further conversation.

When I entered my house, Anthony had left a message scrawled on a torn piece of paper, that read, looking for work. I have to go out of town for the final interview. A job as a truck driver, delivery person has been offered to me. I will return the day after tomorrow. Several days prior, in the morning as I was preparing to leave, and had begun picking up his garments strewn about, there were traces of lipstick on the collar of one of his shirts and a sickening, artificial aroma of gardenias.

Our intimate love times had come to a complete halt. His avoidance of me was a total contrast to the incredible love relation we used to have. There was never an opportunity for conversation because he returned home at night when I was asleep and he slept in the mornings as I got up and prepared to leave for work.

DARLENE'S AWAKENING

I called Lorna and to my surprise, she arrived almost instantly and for the first time, she did not offer the usual utterance of a limited time schedule. I explained my situation. She hugged me and told me not to worry. The words she repeated were, "I understand and luckily it was no worse." What did she mean no worse? What could have been worse than a person taking control of you and your pleadings were ignored? What was worse than not being able to determine who you would choose to share your body with? Under this man's control, I felt powerless, confused, scared and attempted not to allow the hatred I felt towards him overtake me. Even though she expressed concern, there was an almost non- attachment. My sister's concern was genuine, but there was no emotional display. Her stoicism and her emotions were extremely contained?

The name Jackson was a familiar name to most of the residents who lived east of the BAILEY. I knew what services she was purported to assist with, but never had I known anyone who had been to her. Lorna was quite certain about how to link us together and how to advise me as to what I should be prepared for. How did my sister know so much about Mrs. Jackson? It was arranged for us to go to our community abortionist, in the morning, the next day. The fee for local people was fifty dollars. I was going to have one hundred fifty dollars extra. Lorna took charge and made arrangements for the procedure to take place the following morning. So confident was she in making the preparations, the manner in which she demonstrated such awareness or how she knew the procedure so exact was a definite indicator that this would not have been her first meeting. As Lorna and I continued our conversation it became more revealing that she had had a more intimate connection regarding Mrs. Jackson's service.

Before the fire which killed our parents, we all lived together, our mother, my father and our maternal grandmother. My sister and I were at a youth overnight church sleepover when the fire occurred. Our parents were asleep as the house burned down. After the fire, my sister and I began living with Mama Betty, my father's mother. At sixteen, Lorna became pregnant. It was a big embarrassment for the family. In 1946, females were supposed to remain virgins until their wedding night. Were females who never got married, for whatever reason, expected to remain virgins until their demise? Lorna and Larcel who were seventeen have been married since 1947 and are the parents of four children.

Riding along with Lorna whose uncharacteristic silence was somewhat discomforting, creating more uncertainty. Looking out the window, the day was reminiscent of most days this time of year. Muggy air filled the space, no special weather concerns had been reported. An unfamiliar and a very strange stillness seemed to have overtaken everything. The clouds remained stationary, no obvious movement from the wind. It was as if the earth's rotation had halted, had frozen.

With closed eyes, I was holding on very tightly to an awareness I could not define, but I knew the moment I released my grip I could be sucked into a void where all of me would disappear. It was as if everything was being suffocated and there was no escape and knowing what I was headed for had paused my association with all that mattered. My breath did ot follow its usual pattern. Perspiration and a feeling of suffocation was enveloping my body. Lorna became quite concerned and stopped the car to investigate my condition. As she was assured I was stable, she turned on the radio and we continued our journey. Tears were blinding my vision. I was about to extract the life of a baby I had wanted. The music from the radio represented an unremitting clamor pounding channels of my brain until I shouted. "Turn off that radio."

DARLENE'S AWAKENING

As we rode along, Lorna attempted to ease my situation by conversing. I had not the slightest interest in her topics. It was all too much for me when I thought about what was going to take place. There was an interruption in my thought process when Lorna pulled the car to the curb, pointed and said, "that's her house. Don't be afraid Darlene, everything will be okay."

It was exactly nine am when we arrived at Mrs. Dorothy Jackson's little rectangular grey stucco house perched on a slab foundation. This home offered such an extreme contrast to the home where my sexual assault happened. Just when we were prepared to knock, the door was opened by a tall medium built, brown skinned woman. Her manner was welcoming but professional. There were no extra words, only precise directives. The room in which we entered was dark with curtains covering the windows allowing a very small amount of light to enter. Once my eyes adjusted, three chairs, a smaller table between two of the chairs and a coffee table in front of the sofa were visible. They were all arranged in a semi-circle facing the television. On the wall various photos were placed, Some, I assumed were her family members. A large, framed photo of Abraham Lincoln was placed next to the TV on one of the tables. An older man sat in the corner of the sofa watching the television while smoking a cigar. The brief moments I was in his presence the smoke induced nausea. He was deeply engrossed in his program and paid no attention to us. Lorna squeezed my hand very tightly and kissed me on my cheek. Mrs. Jackson must have sensed my discomfort, because very quickly, she ushered me out of the room, instructed me to follow her down the dimly lit hall to another area and offered me a glass of water. I was then directed to a small bathroom and shown antiseptic spray and other materials to sterilize myself before and after that process was completed. She then escorted me to another small room where alcohol, cotton swabs, gauze, scissors, ointments, bandages, bottles of herbs, a stethoscope and other things were on a small table next to the bed. I was instructed to lie on an elevated bed with my knees to the ceiling as she began the procedure. My eyes were closed during the process. Mrs Jackson offered no extraneous conversation, hers was a job to complete with two main objectives; perform the abortion and receive her pay.

Before I had much time to think, I began to cry, uncontrollably. I had no idea I was going to release tears. As my crying gained more momentum, my body began to shake. Mrs. Jackson inquired as to if I were in pain. She was not unfriendly and probably chose not to become personally involved. There was no physical pain, only a hurt in my soul, I was aborting a child, Anthony and I had wanted to have children and now a child I was unable to claim was being sucked out of me. There was more psychological pain as I realized I would not be able to share this experience with the man whom I had loved so dearly. What was my life about? Lost my parents as a child, my very reliable supporter, Mama Betty was gone and more and more distance was developing between my husband and me, the man I had been willing to make many sacrifices for. My sister had stepped up to help me and the gratitude I felt for her was beyond words. I lay there with my eyes closed questioning myself, while attempting to understand the situation I had gotten myself involved in. I asked myself the question I had been examining for the past few months. Was I a prostitute, a whore, a call girl, and now a murderer? These concerns were the origins of the rapidly flowing tears.

When I thought of my Grandmother Betty, I began to pray. "Dear Holy Spirit, please forgive me as I go forward. Please help me to never make this mistake again." Mama constantly said, "God always forgives, and the mistakes we make are our own responsibilities. When we give power to Fear we make choices that can get us into trouble." I didn't understand some of the words, Grandmother spoke, but as I laid on this bed reflecting, I appreciated her wisdom.

The tears lessened, Mrs. Jackson was kind, patient and gentle. After the process was completed, I was given instructions about self- care for the next few days and offered alternatives to prevent future unwanted pregnancies. My obvious impression was that many, many times this task had been performed by her. Perhaps, other females had laid on this bed crying or maybe some having realizations that had previously been locked up.

Once again, I was told to just remain on my back for a few minutes and relax. How many females had to abort because of an unwanted pregnancy? I would have held onto my child had I known what other choices were available to me. I was grateful for my sister, but even with Lorna's care, I felt so very alone, so sad, so angry, so hurt, and so confused. As I laid there looking up at the popcorn textured ceiling with the exposed light bulb dangling from the end of the electric cord. I could hear my Grandmother Betty's words, "trust in the Almighty." Anthony's words would have been different, "God has abandoned Colored folks." I knew I needed to find my own truth and be resolute in it.

Mrs. Jackson led me back to the living room. Just as we were about to exit, the older man who had not made a sound since we first arrived spoke and said, "you gals ought to stop all this stuff, pregnant stuff." It was a good thing I had been taught to respect old people because if he had been able to read my thoughts, he would not have liked them. Mrs. Jackson spoke up and told him to be quiet and instructed us to ignore him. She indicated with nonverbal indications that he was cognitively challenged. I thought even though he might have mental problems, he was aware enough to blame females. Her reference to his unawareness did not ease my anger and frustration about his comment.

Outside again, my eyes readjusted to the bright light. The sun was not yet at its zenith point, but its brightness was intense. I attempted to remain anonymous as I eased into the car. I kept my head lowered in order to not have to relate to anyone. Lorna had already crossed to the other side of the street and was having a conversation with some of the folks who were sitting on their porches appearing devoid of activity, allowing their imaginations to create colorful scenarios about the visitors who go in and come out of the Jackson house across the street.

As I was being driven home, my sister reported that Mrs. Jackson did not live at the house where the abortion took place. According to the neighborly observers, that was her workplace. Each day she and her uncle arrived and stayed a few hours. Occasionally White people came and their fee for her services ranged from three hundred to five hundred dollars. How and where did these nosey neighbors acquire so much information? Had they reached a point where their existences were so devoid of fulfillment that they were willing to allow vicarious snooping to fill a gap? These people, mostly elders similar to the ones I would see each day on my block as I walked to or from the bus alerted me and caused me to realize their examples of sitting on the porches each day, letting life pass by would not be acceptable for me as I grew older.

My grandmother, Mama Betty was different, her days were occupied with baking, working in her garden where she grew all of the vegetables we ate, she cut the grass, repaired what needed to be fixed, attended bible study, was secretary for the church and sang in the choir. She seemed to enjoy her busy schedule and rarely did she sit on her front porch. What was in store for me, I did not know, what I did know was when the age of retirement came, I would not sit and become so involved in the accounts of others and let my inquisitiveness paint their stories in order to give my noninvolvement in life more meaning.

While Lorna drove, she was exuberantly sharing several stories the nosey spectators had related to her, but I had no interest. My first pregnancy had just been terminated. The way Mrs. Jackson conducted her business was of no concern to me. Other people's accounts about the females she treated were not the reason I acquired her services. My number one objective was to hurry home, pull the covers over my head and escape to a private place.

DARLENE'S AWAKENING

Anthony was very agitated as I walked into the house, his attitude was strange and apparently uncomfortable. I did not pay him too much attention because during this period his behavior had become odd and unpredictable. "Who is that woman coming from the back yard?" Lorna yelled. I didn't give her a lot of attention, in fact I didn't have the energy to engage with her or Anthony. My intention was to get in the bed and not converse with anyone. I pulled back the covers and was about to ease into the bed when I saw a hair barrette on the pillow. I never used hairpins, bobby pins or barrettes in my hair. This little ornament in my bed caused me to better understand Anthony's agitation as I entered our home. I had left at the same usual time in the morning. Generally, I returned home at approximately five o'clock. This day because of my ordeal, I came back home at eleven thirty. There was no mention of the barrette on my pillow, the panties or gardenia smelling scarf on the floor in the bathroom. Apparently, my early return prompted much uncertainty. Never did I reference the found objects. My request for Anthony to change the sheets in order for me to get into my bed and relax was quickly obliged without any conversation. As I finally got into my bed, I focused on Lorna's earlier reference about the woman coming out of our backyard and realized I might have been able to connect the face with the artificial gardenia smell.

The private guilt that had been secretly eating away at my conscience had prevented my passing judgment or probing deeply. His evening departures had become more and more accepted. It had become obvious with the scent of cheap artificial gardenia which had attached itself to some of his garments that his buddies who he reported to have been with each evening were not men wearing gardenia perfume. Even when this observation became apparent, my attempt to ignore it brought a sadness that remained constantly.

Deciding what to tell my husband was a major cause of my frustration. I had not been in the habit of lying to him. During those earlier times of our total commitment to each other; those times of our loving innocence with each other; those times when we had bonded as a unit with no separation, we had agreed to be honest with each other, no matter what the circumstances might have been. Having seen lipstick and the putrid artificial flower smell on his shirt, few days prior and now a barrette on my pillow, panties and a gardenia scented scarf on the bathroom floor, a revelation I was no longer able to ignore forced me to accept the fact, that he too was also keeping secrets and not being totally honest with me. This revelation was a justification for my concocting whatever story I would share with him.

For the next few weeks an uncomfortable and strangely unfamiliar bond we shared. No longer was food prepared as I arrived home. We remained polite to each other, but there was an unprecedented distance. The relationship that had developed between us had become similar to that of the Coodes, my employers. He did not know the full details of my situation because I informed him that I was having female troubles and Lorna had been helping me to feel better.

One and a half weeks after the abortion, I returned to work. Mrs. Coode left a note reminding me of a multitude of job duties because everything had piled up in my absence, there was no inquiry about my condition. Invisibility! What must he have told her? There had been no inquiring phone calls from her. For the next two weeks, Mr. Coode ignored me or at least he never pursued me.

At home the distance between my beloved and me was becoming further and further. Anthony was only present in the mornings lying asleep as I got up and prepared for the day. When I returned in the early evenings, his presence was non- existent. I would fix my dinner, an activity I didn't have much care for or have experience with. However, to my surprise on this particular evening, Anthony was at home and had prepared another of his fabulous meals: fish, macaroni and cheese, mustard greens, sliced tomatoes and for dessert, sweet potato pie.

DARLENE'S AWAKENING

Memories from the past were darting in and out of my consciousness. Perplexed was I, as the memory of an artificial, gardenia aroma suffocated my senses. Before I continued to mentally question the experience, Anthony, who had been distant since we sat down interrupted with his questions. "Why did you go to Mrs. Jackson's house with Lori?

I know what happens at that house, I know what that woman does. I also know that Lori was six months pregnant and had no need for the service. Why did you go there? What have you been doing and who have you been screwing? Damn Darlene, what have you been doing, When? Where? Why?"

He didn't allow me to speak, his didn't yell, but his voice was several decibels above mine, filled with much emotion each time I tried to say something. Finally, I chose not to attempt to talk. He insisted that he loved me and no one would ever love me as he had. He spoke non-stop, more than he had conversed with me for many months. He said, "you cheated on me, because I was not able to impregnate you. I couldn't get you pregnant no matter what I did or did not do, so you went out and found another man. You looked at me with pity. I don't want your pity or your feeling sorry for me. Maybe I ain't the kind of man who has lots of money and other things, but I am a man. Nobody will ever love you as much as me. I Am A Man, but I ain't whole. "Who is your God?" And still he spoke, and I was not permitted to comment.

Finally, before I was aware of my emotional strength, I yelled, "you are a quitter, you never complete anything. How dare you say those things to me. Do not behave like you are a saint with your disgusting smell of cheap, artificial gardenia. All you ever do is blame, blame, blame. It is never about anything you have done that may be wrong. You have no idea about what happened to me and you do not care, because it is always about you and how bad everybody is treating you and everything is always about you, you, you."

The power I had allowed to spring forth shocked me and must have done the same to him because he had never heard me raise my voice in such a way. He stopped talking for a moment, looked at me and very slowly repeated, "you cheated on me." The anger had mounted up in me because he never once asked me what I had to say of if I had something important to share. He immediately began attacking me. Now as I look back at the situation, I realize all he was thinking about was himself, possibly all he ever thought about was himself.

The more he talked about me, almost as if I were not there, the angrier I became. Had I also become invisible to him? I had been willing to do whatever it took to keep us together. Was it okay for there to have been panties, a scarf and a barrette that belonged to another female in my bedroom and bathroom? It was at that moment my anger really resurfaced at his allegations. After his loud accusations and the many attempts to insert my perspective were ignored a frustration sprung forth and generated a power I had never before accessed and was not familiar with. My ordinarily calm demeanor had been uprooted, agitated and compromised like the trees during a winter storm where the ferocity of the winds dismantled everything in its path. All that remained of me was a prickled empty shell protecting particles of me that were fighting for survival. Somewhere buried in my private chambers an explosion of utterances emanated and shook my foundation causing me to grab hold to a chair for support. He became momentarily quiet as I spewed words that a church-girl would have been disassociated with.

His uncaring attitude about my situation, his accusations without a degree of concern were based on his infidelity. Mama Betty used to say," as you think, so you are." Never did he inquire as to my situation, never was there an expression of any degree of concern. Had he had a moment of clarity he may have considered the fact that we were always together except when I was away at work or when he made his nightly rendezvous returning to our bed very early in the morn as the roosters announce a new day. What I had accepted as a forever connection was my perception alone. What I had come to realize was that our words and actions were not sharing an equal platform. Why did he think it was acceptable for him to be indiscreet? Did he think his indiscretion would prove that he was a man? I had never questioned him about his nightly escapades or the fact that for several months, he had begun treating me as if I were a stranger. I had almost become invisible to my husband whom I had loved so unconditionally. He was never present any longer when I was at home.

Those past Sunday afternoons when we spent happier times together had become nonexistent. His suitcases which had been obstructed from my view by a table had not been visible until he walked over and picked them up. He was at the door and was just about to go out when I handed him a little package with a barrette, panties and a gardenia-scented scarf. We both had tears gently streaming down our cheeks. I watched him as he walked out of the house, went down the steps, entered his car, never looked back and drove away. That was four years ago and the last time I saw my Anthony. His departure was not a complete surprise, because Anthony's pattern had been to quit and place blame. His ability to commit fully had not been one of his strongest traits. His ego was devastated when he was told he would not be able to reproduce. Feeling less than a man because of some of the daily ordeals, unable to impregnate me, discovering that his partner had had an abortion, provided enough fuel to ignite a change. Our earlier, happier times were the ones I have chosen to remember. As I am about to graduate from college, the contrast of who I was and who I am has provided much fuel for the new me I am becoming.

A SOLITARY REALITY

The morning bus ride the day after my husband's departure was typical except when our town drunk, Walter Jenkins boarded. As soon as he got on the bus, he immediately began his rant. " I may look like a fool, dress like a fool, act like a fool or talk like a fool, think like a fool, but I ain't no fool." The entire time he was ranting, he was laughing and winking his left eye. His slight imbalance caused him to lean to one side with his right hand placed on his right hip. The bus driver yelled, 'sit down Walter and stop the racket. We are about to cross the BAILEY." "Did you say BAILEY? Let me off this here damn bus now, I may act like a fool, I may talk like a fool, but I ain't no fool. Let me off this here damn bus right now. I ain't riding this here bus cross no river." Most passengers were laughing as the bus halted and he departed. On this particular morning, even the very serious bible readers paused momentarily and joined in. The bus continued, with the riders looking out their windows at him staggering onto the pedestrian ramp going across the river. His antics were perfect to help me forget my bitter experience. For a brief moment, I wondered if Anthony was embraced with the woman who smelled like artificial, cheap gardenias. We bus riders laughed at Mr. Jenkins, but I concentrated on what his story must have been to have given him a life where so early in the day, he was already inebriated.

For the next weeks after my beloved had left, a new downward spiral into an indefinable endless destination seemed to be my journey. My nights were endless and sleepless. The slumber I craved avoided me. Anthony had adopted the habit of leaving each evening and returning after I had gone to sleep. It had become commonplace and accepted. Even though I felt alone and abandoned at least I knew in the morning when I woke up he would be lying next to me; however, once he walked out the door with his suitcases and drove away, it was if my heart were weeping while my rational self was going in circles surrounding itself and at its nucleus was a deep dark bottomless hole where no light was coming through. Attempting to make sense out of what had become a seemingly impossible situation created weeks and months of pain and instability.

DARLENE'S AWAKENING

At work, my extra- curricular job obligation continued. A twenty - dollar bill lay next to the six dollars each time, I leased my body. Referring to it this way helped me to soothe my acceptance. I surrendered my body with my arms at my sides, palms facing up to the sky. If a feeling of pleasure was ignited because a slight sensation surged, I clenched my teeth together, and thought of those times with Anthony. I did not allow this man any reaction from me. The guilt that had been shadowing me had lessened but I blamed this man lying on top of me for my Anthony having left, even though I knew my reasoning was not totally true, it helped me to rationalize my actions or non -actions.

On the evening return, looking out the window as the east-bound bus crossed the BAILEY, and approached Linden and G streets, there were usually three or four women on the corner waiting to be picked up by men they would sexually serve.

These women in their form–fitting attire exposing more of their bodies than was the norm had been the objects of my derision as I had judged them each time. Now, I realized how similar we were. A major difference was my paid sexual activity was in a fancy home with the same aggressor who paid me well. These females gave their bodies to strangers at various locations and if they had a "pimp," or a madam, that person had complete control of their money. As I looked at these women, the question plaguing my mind was why they chose to sell their bodies. Perhaps, it had not been their solitary decision. Had circumstances beyond their control forced them into a life of sexual servitude? Did they have the shame I was enduring? Were they living in a secret world where their desire for comfort came in the caress of strangers? They appeared to wear their identity as a badge of pride or was it just a cover up for their true feelings that were raging with no promise of anything tangible.

Some bible readers momentarily allowed the action on the corner to compete with their devoted obsession. A few were stealing glances out the windows but appeared unnecessarily uncomfortable for fear of not earning a place in the promised land that was awaiting their arrival. The ladies on the corner were generally smoking cigarettes, wearing smiles and engaged in raucous conversation as they waited. How astonished I was on a day as the wind was blowing while redirecting articles in its path when one of the women whose skirt blew up and revealed her uncovered private female area. Fortunately, the bus continued before passengers were able to get an unobstructed view. A few gasps could be heard from those who were allegedly engrossed with their bibles.

How could I judge these ladies, or anyone based on what I had involuntarily given consent to? My vision of me was blurred and unclear. A part of me was buried at a depth with a disconnection from anything that might force me to examine myself more objectively. This disconnect made it easy for me to redirect my truth while allowing fear for my sexual abuse to control my actions thus placing blame and accepting no responsibility. This let me have an attitude of superiority as I observed the women, who frequented the corner. As I later began to restore, forgive and reorganize my awareness of self, I had to provide an honest assessment of what I had grown to accept and have a more truthful relationship with me and not place all blame on the aggressor. I had focused on the assumption of my role as a poor victim which was an easy way not to have to face responsibility for my own participation. The women who sell their bodies for sex have been defined as, prostitutes, whores, call girls, ladies of the night, harlots, sluts, streetwalkers, trollops, or others. What was my title, I wondered, who was I? These thoughts I pondered while walking to my house, from the bus stop.

There they were., the same neighbors, usually those who had retired; the ones who sat on their porches early in the mornings as I passed by heading to the bus stop to go to work appeared to be glued to their same locations when I returned. What did they do all day?

DARLENE'S AWAKENING

Entering my home, alone I reflected on those earlier days, the meals Anthony used to prepare when our life was in harmony. I remembered a perfect breeze that cleansed the environment, his gorgeous smile that brought in light where there was darkness and life was so sweet. How I missed those times. Since he left, I realized each morning I rushed to get out of the house. The memories were too severe, like daggers piercing my innards. My appreciation for this home where I had grown up had unraveled bitter memories where I no longer felt welcomed.

Arriving at my job, the following day all things remained the same. My fee was on the table along with my daily work agenda. I cleaned, and just as I was completing my assignments, Byron Coode quietly approached me as he always did, turned me around to face him and laid me on the shag rug in the pink room. Why did he continuously turn me to face him? Had my invisibility lessened? Maybe since I was not considered to be an equal human, it was easy for him to assault me, because I appeared to be a willing receiver who did not resist as I had previously, he felt no guilt. He had now begun to kiss me with each interaction. He kissed me from head to foot. My behavior was tantamount to that of a statue. What had become of me? Had I allowed the money he paid me to override my sense of decency? It had become difficult for me to face myself in the mirror. An unresponsive receiver I was, but still I received. The only sounds ever emanated were his. Mr. Coode's sounds had become much louder than when he first began his abuse. I remained stationary while he moved the parts of my body he wanted to access. Occasionally, I heard him repeat,' I love you." Repeatedly as he was kissing me all over my body, he would repeat "I love you, I love you. You taste so good. Aren't I good to you?"

I never answered, how could I? Generally, his words and actions created a conflicting puzzle because in his moments of passion when the love references were spoken versus the completion of each encounter where immediately afterwards, he quickly got up, seemed extremely embarrassed did not look at me, did not utter any words or other acknowledgement went into the bathroom and when finished, got into his car and drove away.

On an unforgettable day, as he released and let out a long satisfying sigh, a loud interruption cancelled the moment. "Byron, what is wrong with you? Are you out of your mind? I knew there was distance between us, but this, what will everyone think? You are fucking a Nigger!! Are you insane? All of you, mother, daddy, Jason and Mindy are always telling me I am insane. What do you think they would say? Byron, a Nigger, how could you bring such shame to this family? Have you lost your mind? You reject me for a Nigger! Don't you understand, I represent perfection, alabaster skin, blue eyes and blonde hair? What more could you want? I have never understood you and now this. You are an embarrassment to our kind. In this beautiful room, how could you soil it with this Nigger? What is the matter with you?" Remaining motionless, there was no recollection as to if I had been breathing. In a moment of suspension my entire being had become frozen, unsure of what action to take. This aspect of her personality had never been revealed to me before. She was screaming multiple swear words, using hand gestures, throwing pink figurines Mr. Coode who was naked from his waist down moved off of me and said to his wife, "You do not understand." Those were the only words he uttered.

So involved were they in their conversation that I was ignored and able to slowly and carefully redress as I put on my brassiere, panties and pink uniform. Had I been able to, I would have excused myself and run away, but I did not know how to. She never looked at me, only at him. My invisibility again manifested, I didn't count as a complete human, as an equal, thus it was easy to dismiss me as if I did not matter, as someone who was less than. The tag Nigger served its purpose for her. It was not the name, but the feeling of superiority, disdain for the domestic worker whose only value was one of service. The vitriol she released was surprising, never had I known she was able to produce such rage. Janice continued for what seemed forever. Discomfort that was produced in my head, and in my stomach increased my anger and my fear. Having no idea as to how this interlude would end, made me become increasingly nervous. Her loudness and his uncertainty were frightening and extremely aggressive intrusions into my stability.

DARLENE'S AWAKENING

That alone feeling I had been observing in myself since Anthony left sprang forth. I had nowhere to run, there was nothing for me to grasp, suddenly my stomach began hurting, I was sweating, mucus was running down my face, a nervous energy I had never experienced before was overtaking my sense of control, all parts of my body were shaking. Each attempt to manage my fear was in vain and I quietly began uncontrollably sobbing again. They were the same sobs I released the night Anthony left, the same sobs I encountered when I had the abortion. These two people, Janice and Byron were so involved in their exchange that my presence did not matter. Escaping from the horrible situation was foremost in my thoughts, but how? It was as if an intense pain was piercing my being, my soul, my essence. The light coming in through the curtains seemed to fluctuate from light to dark. What had I done, what had I become involved in? Why? Why? Why? I asked myself again and again. Lying there having my own private conversation had taken me away from the real situation that was taking place.

I opened my eyes because the screaming had come to an abrupt halt. Janice removed a small revolver from her purse. I quickly remembered the words she shared with her friend about the necessity of carrying a pistol in her purse. She repeated in an almost inaudible voice, "how could I live with someone who had laid down with a Nigger?" He said to her, "Calm down Janice, it is not as bad as it looks. Let me explain." I wondered what he meant. Was I about to be killed? Was she going to kill both of us? It was at that precise moment I asked Jesus to please help me. There was no response from anywhere because in the next instant, she put the gun to her head, pulled the trigger which produced a loud sound and sprayed blood all over the pink carpet, pink lamp, pink sofa and the figurines on the table. He got up, rushed to her saying, "forgive me, forgive me, forgive me, you just didn't understand." He held her head in his naked lap and began to cry. I slowly sat up, still in a state of confusion not knowing what to do. Gradually, I regained myself, went to the worker's room, redressed and was about to exit when he entered. He had put his clothes back on, never looked into my eyes, but handed me five hundred dollars and said in a voice with no emotion, "take it, leave and don't come back." This was the same man who less than an hour before had been kissing all over my body, repeating I love you and was now unable to look at me. His behavior was if I had killed her. Again, I was reminded as to how I was just an object for him to relieve his feelings, and his frustrations. Maybe to him my invisibility and my visibility were in conflict.

The ugly pink uniform I was required to wear each day was quickly discarded into the trash can as I rushed away from that house. My feet would not move fast enough. Unaware of the fact that I had been running down the hill to the bus stop until I almost lost my balance. I slowed myself down, attempted to gain composure, wiped my face, cleared away tears that were blinding my vision and blew my nose. The pounding, repetitive words, "forgive me, forgive me," echoed and echoed.

DARLENE'S AWAKENING

As I approached the bus stop, there were other Domestics I had never seen before. I assumed I looked a mess to them, because the emotions had overtaken my objectivity. Their judgements or non-judgements were of no concern to me. My physical body was standing at the bus stop, but my mental body had escaped into an uncontrollable, spiraling prism. catapulting through the constellations endeavoring to reunite with a more satisfying conclusion. A bystander's loud sneeze jarred me back. Fortunately, no conversation transpired because I had left an hour and a half earlier than usual, and consequently there was no recognition of any of these workers. The questions and curiosities may have been too much for me. I did not look at anyone and no one spoke to me. With a bowed head, eyes focused on the ground, I noticed that everything appeared in order, each stone in this sidewalk configuration was perfectly, equidistantly placed. In my neighborhood, most of the lawns were trimmed and cared for but in this area all the lawns were perfectly manicured, flowers were lined up uniformly and the variations were almost non-existent. The reds, the blues, the yellows were organized. No things seemed out of order. The yards and porches were vacant unlike the yards and porches in my neighborhood where there was always activity. Were these exteriors like the interiors? The years I had walked up and down this hill, I had never given much thought to these concerns until today as I was awaiting the bus. From the outside all looked perfect. I wondered if there were dark, dark secrets through the portals of these seemingly ideal edifices. As I looked at the ground, I observed ants busily moving pieces much larger than themselves, did the insects have secrets?

Several hours later or so it felt, the bus arrived; however, it had been only twenty minutes. I boarded, found a seat and was unaware I had been crying. The tears must have been flooding because a woman sitting next to me offered me a tissue. My shame was such that I refused, turned away and took out my own tissue and attempted to control my sadness. Ordinarily, I would have seen a familiar face, but on this earlier trip no one was recognizable.

Amid all of these unfamiliar Domestics, I was alone, scared and needed someone, somebody, anything. As I observed the passengers on the bus, they appeared to duplicate the ones on my usual bus. Many of the women were reading their Bibles. What would they have done without these books? Did their Bibles supply the solutions they had been reaching for? Were their Bibles the sources that appeased their longings when the pain, rejection and hurt became much more than could be explained? Had their work experiences challenged them to a point where they had been barely able to grasp?

I had again become lost in my private world, and mentally severing connections with my physical surroundings. The bus began filling up with loud, teenagers exhibiting their lack of civility and undisciplined clamor while yelling from the front to the back of the bus. Each time the bus hit a bump there was a loud clanking sound. The kids would pause in between and wait for the sound. "Hey Melvin and Clarice, is that the sound you make when you are loving?" All of them were laughing and screaming with a repetitive chant, "when you're loving, when you're loving." Some of the language being used would have shocked the elders. I was almost twenty-two and didn't think I was so old, but many of their comments astonished me. Looking at the advertisements above the windows, one stood out, "For Peace and Life Eternal, Repent and be Saved," featured a picture of Reverend Collins, the very familiar minister at Union Baptist Church where lots of Negroes in our community went for consolation. I was certain many of their parents and grandparents attended that place of worship. Apparently, these behaviors were daily rituals. The other riders and the driver ignored the outrageous outpourings. When the bus arrived at Pine and Lake Streets, many people got off. Again, teens began their chant," when you're loving, when you're loving." Whoever Melvin and Clarice were must have gotten off also, because once the bus continued its route again, the remaining teenagers were relatively quiet.

DARLENE'S AWAKENING

After what seemed like an inordinate amount of time the bus arrived at my departure point. As I got off the bus and began walking my daily route, I was reminded of the degree of awareness which had been so implanted that even if my eyes had been closed, my exact location would have been apparent. and I could have arrived safely at home. Each crack in the pavement, the holes in different areas of walls where stones were missing, each mailbox with its uniqueness, each tree with blossoms indicating the seasons, those were some of the landmarks I knew very well. The images had been embedded in my mind since I was a little girl walking along this sidewalk with my grandmother and Lorna, times when going back and forth to the market, maybe strolling along as a teenager, this path had had minor changes.

As usual there were people in their yards or on their porches. The five houses from the bus stop to my house were all similar, older Victorian two stories with attics. People were generally tending to their yards, painting or repairing something.

The first home as I departed the bus was that of the Chows, a family of four generations whose ancestors had come from China, decades ago. This family lived together and operated a small grocery store that was attached to their house. I recall that small store had everything or anything a person needed. There were needles and thread, pens, paper, hammers, nails in one section and the food area had selections of fish, chicken, vegetables, fruit and much more.

Grandmother Betty knew these people well and had learned a few Mandarin phrases, in fact she seemed to know everyone well, not just on our block but for many blocks in our neighborhood. In addition, she could repeat Italian, Spanish and some Jewish phrases. Her understanding and apparent friendships with so many people had always amazed me.

The Boticelli's dog Barlo was able to look through a cyclone fence that bordered his home with a clear view of the bus stop. He would bark incessantly as I got off the bus until I was near his home. Guido, one of the children told me Barlo did not have that relationship with anyone else. The closer my approach, the quieter he became. Acknowledging him was one of my daily obligations, mainly because he demanded it. Ours was a beautiful non-verbal relationship. We walked parallel to each other, with a cyclone fence and a few plants separating us. Barlo in his yard and I walked along on the sidewalk until we reached the end of his yard. I would look at him and say, "See you Barlo." He would bark once as I continued homeward. On that particular day, we had our usual walk together, but he quietly whimpered the entire time. I felt that he must have been sensing my grief. It was a very personal relationship the two of us shared.

Mr. Williams who lived with his sister and her three kids was another of those people who could tell you about everyone and all events in the neighborhood. His knowledge of the activities on our block was another curiosity because I had never seen him anywhere except sitting in his chair on his porch. Where and how did he acquire the community information? If a person lingered, Mr. Williams would sometimes share the latest neighborhood gossip, but always inserted into the conversation was the way in which he warned his deceased wife.

"I told Letty to stop eating so much pork, beef and salt. She ate it at every meal. Her blood pressure shot up, her heart got bad, she had a stroke and she died. I miss my wife, but she would not listen. Sometimes, I would walk on the other side of the street to avoid him. When I was ten years old, I had secretly adopted him to be my replacement grandfather. Today, he was curious as to why I had come home so early. He looked at me and wanted to know if everything was okay. I had stopped crying and had cleaned my face before I exited the bus, but he was able to detect something about my condition. Lorna once told me he had special powers. I did not know where my sister obtained such information, but his attitude towards me was very strange on that day. I told him I hadn't been feeling well. I did not know what Mr. Williams must have sensed, he expressed a very deep concern for me and told me if ever I needed anything to let him know because I was a good girl. Those words tore at my heart, because they seemed like such a big, horrible lie. He had always reminded me of the grandfather I wished I had. Both of my grandfathers had died when I was a child. Never would I have shared with Mr. Williams what I had been involved in. I thanked him for his kindness and hurried away from his stare.

Mrs. Geraldine Jones who was my immediate next-door neighbor, was friendly and always appeared occupied. Her skin was very light and the local gossip was that she passed. This woman was a good neighbor, her racial identity was her private choice. Grandmother's slogan was, "live and let live and if we took care of ourselves, we would have a big enough job." Geraldine was the community seamstress with a daily flow of customers that came and went each day. The four people who were employed by her would come in the morning and leave in the late afternoon. An occasional car or truck would unload bolts of fabric, boxes of threads, and sewing accessories. The curtains at the Barnett Hotel for its fifteen rooms plus the huge dining room had been made by Geraldine and her employees. Choir robes for churches, wedding gowns and dresses for bridesmaids were some of her creations. There was a time Mrs. Jones offered Anthony a job, but he refused and told me that was not the kind of job a real man would want. I had not a clue as to what the job required, but he refused.

Arriving home, I rushed to undress, tossed my clothes into the trash in the hopes that the remaining memories would also be tossed out. Feeling extremely dirty, inside and outside, I took a lengthy bath, washed my hair in an effort to clean the stench I had stepped into. After I cleaned my body, oiled, powdered, perfumed it, put on my pajamas, and made a cup of hot chocolate, I sat down to bring some clarity to a muddled situation. Over and over, I questioned my participation that awful day. Janice Coode was a strange woman who, had treated me as if I didn't exist or matter, but still I would not have wished harm to come to her. I was praying and asking for lucidity and forgiveness when the phone rang. Roxanne Bruebaker, the aunt of Byron Coode introduced herself. I became nervous and suspicious until she told me Mr. Coode had recommended me with utmost praise and shared the horrible situation, I had been a witness to. She asked me if I needed a job. I answered in the affirmative. She then inquired as to if I wanted to come the next day or because of such a horrible occurrence take a few days off. I assured her that I was okay and preferred to begin the next day. Mrs. Bruebaker gave me her address and said she looked forward to meeting me. Her comments were unexpected. This entire incident had become mystifying, and much too much for me to understand. I had no idea this man would have recommended me for anything. His attitude towards me was always so distant and strange except when our bodies met.

I didn't sleep that night, Janice and Bryon Coode's words echoed. When my eyes were closed, I saw the blood splattered in the pink room, heard her screams when she first discovered us, heard the gunshot, saw her limp body and him holding her head with blood escaping onto his lap and his tears running down on her unmoving face. The horror of it all, the scene would not go away. The first rays of sun, welcoming the new day were a relief, offering a direction away from the past. Jumping out of bed, performing my morning ritual,rushing from the house to catch the bus, I realized I was almost running to get to the bus stop. It was an attempt to get away from myself. An impossible escape, but yesterday's memories were overpowering my thoughts. It was as if I were in an upside- down spiral where no beginning or ending was apparent.

Sixth Chapter

PROBLEMS SOLUTIONS

LOVE YOURSELF

I boarded the bus and nothing had changed. The same bus with its smell of bleach, insecticide, vomit, the same driver and the same cast of characters who boarded, excited and performed their daily rituals. Everything remained the same, only I felt different, something I could not describe. An aroused, uncomfortable energy circulating in my body prevented me from a relaxing surrender.

Arriving at the street where I used to exit, the other domestics who I used to walk up and down the hill with each day looked curiously at me as they got off the bus and I remained seated. Eight more bus stops, I got off the bus in a strange, very unfamiliar section of town. More trees were present than structures. In every direction the color green was in profusion. Slowly I became more focused and realized I was in a small forest.

Birds of many colors and sizes were in profusion. Some of these flying Ones I had never seen before. . They appeared happily as they were flitting from branch to destinations beyond my view. Were they free from predators? Their melodies provided a continuous harmony. What beautiful freedom these freely flying ones symbolized.

Some of the trees were reaching the clouds. Never had I seen such vegetation. There was a freshness in the air enveloping the space as I breathed in deeply. Appreciating this newly discovered natural environment provided an opportunity for a more positive focus. A juxtaposition, from the horrors of the past few months.

Walking down the driveway, I approached the perfectly perched storybook home sitting in a clearing atop a gently, sloping hill, painted in very subdued earthen colors.

Having arrived at 1624 Leslie Drive, I knocked on the front door. A medium sized White lady with shoulder length speckled grey hair wearing a baggy smock, loose fitting pants and an apron with many pockets, each filled with paint brushes opened the door wearing a big smile. "Hello, you must be Darlene. You are lovely! Come on in and relax." "Yes, I am Darlene." "Please remove your shoes, we do not wear shoes inside the house." Never before had I been asked not to wear my shoes inside. Had I known I would be required to be barefoot, I would have painted my toenails. Mrs. Roxanne Bruebaker's manner was not at all what I had expected. She was very warm and friendly. I had never met a White person who was so friendly and kind without even knowing anything about me. We went into her dining room where she gestured for me to sit and make myself comfortable. This experience and her behavior were unfamiliar to me. She excused herself and returned with a pitcher of lemonade and two glasses. This woman, a White woman was going to sit at the same table, just a few feet from me and allow me to drink from one of her glasses with her. It was as if she was not aware of my color or race, as if she didn't care about those things. It was the first time I was engaged in conversation with a White person and felt comfortable and entirely present. Roxanne was so patient as I nervously blundered while attempting to explain a little information about me. She listened as I answered her questions without dismissing my statements; she looked directly into my eyes. I was not Invisible to her. Mrs. Bruebaker asked me many questions about myself and shared her sympathy for the horrible situation I had had to endure.

DARLENE'S AWAKENING

Her living room was so inviting with many pillows, two sofas, lots of books, a fireplace, and a wide array of things. Some of the items she showed me were from places she had traveled. Roxanne had been to places all over the world. Most of the locations she shared I had never heard of before; Rapanui, Stonehenge, Machu Picchu, Angkor Wat. There were masks from Africa, Thailand and China, beautiful hand-woven blankets from South America; she had skied in Switzerland; fell in love in Paris and had eaten some of the most delicious food while visiting Italy. I felt very satisfied and comfortable in that room. We sat and talked for about an hour. She told me she didn't need a housekeeper, but at the insistence of her nephew she called me. He told her that I was a good worker and a good person. When she repeated what he had said, I felt a sudden reaction in my stomach. In the years I had worked for the Coodes, he had never spoken more than ten words to me and to hear that he had given such a positive recommendation was more than I knew how to handle. I was quiet as she led me around her house. There was no back room for workers.

The place she called her Sanctuary, her studio was in a separate building, adjacent to the house. We entered a huge room with high ceilings that were much larger than the other rooms in the house. Paintings of all sizes and shapes filled the space, a few were in a separate area that would be used in her upcoming exhibit. I didn't really know what she was talking about. This was my first time being in an artist studio. There were huge paintings on the walls, mostly beautiful landscapes of water, the night sky, clouds, sunsets, trees, children, older people and some of the images didn't represent anything I had ever seen.

She told me she was a professional artist and was preparing for an exhibit. The one exhibit I had ever gone to was when I was a senior in high school and our art class had an exhibit for one week. Paintings and drawings donned the walls in the main halls of the school. As I reflected, I remembered there was no comparison to the high-school exhibit and what I was being shown.

Roxanne told me she didn't like to be disturbed when she was painting and that I was welcome to paint also if ever I wanted to.

Next was the Growth Room where I was instructed to always relax and take a deep breath before entering. Food and water of any kind were never ever to be in that room. Words in different colors and designs on the door read: renew, regenerate, wake up to your true self, forgiveness, happiness, joy, truth, peace, generosity, kindness, prosperity, laughter, love yourself, love others. This was the room for me to use for my personal growth. I had no idea what she was talking about. As we went in through the door, we descended approximately two feet into a concave room, a space like none I had ever seen before. The floor coverings that gently swallowed my feet were also in shades of warm blues, not as dark as cobalt and not as light as powder blue. Also, the walls were obscured with a medium soft, blue, flexible fabric, as were the pillows of all sizes. In the middle of the room suspended from the ceiling was a golden colored, metal- framed pyramid structure. Why the pyramid? It was strange to me. "What did she mean when she said, "a room I was to use for my personal growth?"

Roxanne led me to other areas in her home. Each room was entirely different with its own unique signature. Another extremely pleasant section next to the kitchen where a large variety of plants added to the environment. The room had a retractable ceiling and windows where at the push of a button, they would open up and allow breezes to enter through the screens or close when necessary.

Her artistry was evident with choices of colors and details I may never have considered. One of the three bedrooms was entirely white, the walls, ceilings, soft flowing curtains, large white throw rugs on hardwood floors, the bed coverings were white feather comforters and in the ceiling was a huge skylight. According to Roxanne on nights when the moon was not visible, she would lie in her bed, look out at the night sky and become one with the Cosmos. She spoke in ways I had never heard before;" become one with the Cosmos. " I wondered what she was talking about. I began to think that Mrs. Bruebaker might also be weird, but I liked her. I remembered Mama Betty's words, "keep an open mind, keep an open heart and there will be many new things to learn and experience." I never fully knew what she was teaching me, but Grandmother's words were beginning to have more relevance.

DARLENE'S AWAKENING

The garden and a small orchard were reminiscent of photographic depictions in magazines. Beautiful flowers of all colors and descriptions growing low to the ground, others hanging. Several types of flowers emitted fragrances that perfumed the surroundings. Mrs. Bruebaker made special mention of the gardenia plants which were blooming in profusion. The mention of the word gardenia stirred up memories of Anthony and his secret rendezvous. She handed me one of the flowers and told me to keep it close to my heart and allow its loveliness to erase anything that might have caused unhappiness. There was a flash of thought as I remembered the artificially putrid, gardenia smell embedded in some of Anthony's garments. At her insistence, I held the flower and absorbed its fragrance. The delicately sweet, natural, fragrant aroma with its pure white velvety petals offered a vibrance with no comparison.

Fruits, vegetables and herbs filled in the remainder of the space. Many of the plants I was unfamiliar with. She invited me to work in the garden whenever I chose. Roxanne informed me that whenever she was not in her studio painting, she would put many hours into her yard. The gardeners would come every week but were not permitted to disturb her plants.

In addition to painting, working in the garden was her other favorite thing to do. Based on the beauty and perfection of the plants, it was obvious they were well cared for. She assured me whenever time permitted and she was not engaged in the studio, she donated many hours to caring for her "babies" as she called them.

I had worked a small amount with my Grandmother in her Plot. More than growing the plants, I remembered listening to the stories she told me about her life as a young girl. She had attended school in a one-room building with children from elementary age to eight -grade. Mama Betty finished all of the required classes but there were no other schools in the Negro area for her to attend. She was excited when I graduated from high school and shared my diploma with everyone who visited our home. Grandmother said, getting a high school diploma would be one of my most important achievements in the future. It was embarrassing when she showed my diploma to everyone, our neighbors, even our mailman, and bragged about how I had finished school. She would have been proud had Lorna graduated, but becoming pregnant as a high-school senior prevented the completion of her studies.

Growing tomatoes, and a few other vegetables, with Mama in her garden had been very limited. Digging in the ground, uncovering worms did not appeal to me. My Grandmother explained how important they were to help make the soil good. I did not care to have to touch those slimy, wiggly creatures. She always had a reasonable explanation for everything. I gradually became more comfortable, more relaxed and reluctantly accepted the idea that worms were necessary for good soil and helped to insure healthy plants. I worked outdoors with Mama mainly because I loved listening as she shared some of her stories. Everything had been growing well, my tomato plants had medium sized fruits. It was on that horrible day when I saw a monster sized lime green worm with horns crawling up the vine, I shouted so loudly and scared Mama. She laughed and laughed, walked over, picked up the worm and explained the metamorphosis of the creature which would turn into a moth. Sitting in a comfortable chair with a good book was more appealing than digging in the soil. It was because of Grandma Betty's apparent pleasure as she connected with the earth that I relaxed more whenever I accompanied her with planting.

Maybe in the future I would honor Mrs. Bruebaker's garden invitation, it was a beautiful place. Just as she was turning away to leave, Roxanne said, "there is food in the refrigerator and a delicious freshly made sweet-potato pie. Eat whatever you want. I do not need anything. I will be working in my studio most of the day. Sit in the Growth room relax, take a nap and listen." This new woman was kind and likeable, but many of the things she talked about flew over my head, I had no idea. What did she mean, listen? There would be no one else in the room, who was I to listen to? I didn't know her well enough to ask. She returned to her studio and I was left wandering about attempting to relax in this new environment.

I wanted to help but had no idea how to. The countless magazines in various places all had copies of her paintings with her name attached. I wandered about looking for a job chore. It was uncomfortable to just stroll around not knowing what to do. In a new home with a new employer, who offered no guidance or direction was puzzling for me. One of the magazine articles revealed that Roxanne and Phillip Bruebaker had been married for thirty-five years. He had died in an avalanche as he was scaling the Himalayas ten years ago. The couple had adopted a nephew, Byron who was a college lecturer and a very successful Financial Advisor. Shivers ran up my spine as I read the article.

There was nothing for me to do, would I be able to continue this job? Working for the Coodes was my first and only regular employment. As a teenager, I would sometimes baby-sit, but that kind of work was temporary and just supplied enough money for me to pay for my ticket to go to the movie theater. That job with the Coodes came about because my grandmother had arranged it. I did not know the details. Sitting alone in Mrs. Brubacker's living room with much uncertainty, again I reflected on how my Mama Betty seemed to always be able to find solutions. Where would I go to find more work? Who would I talk to? As I sat and read magazines, I realized it was a first -time occurrence for me. My invisibility in a White person's home had disappeared, but I felt idle and of no use. Also, I was reminded of Mama Betty saying, "an idle mind is the devil's workshop." If Roxanne were painting each day or working in her garden, how was she able to maintain such a clean and a dust free home? The floors, the walls, in fact everything appeared to be pristine.

Back to the Growth Room, I entered slowly, carefully and sat down directly under the pyramid and was totally encumbered in an ocean of blueness. She had told me to listen, I attempted, but was unable to hear anything. Suddenly as I relaxed, I experienced a sensation where my body began to feel differently. It is difficult to explain the sensation, but immediately my body felt lighter. It felt so good, a feeling I had never ever had before. It was different from the pleasurable feelings I had when Anthony and I were in our beautiful intense moments of intimacy. This was new for me, my body succumbed to this pleasurable feeling and it was as if I had been floating above everything, not just in this Growth Room, but high in the heavens. I cannot explain what happened but the next thing I remembered was opening my eyes, looking up and observing the pyramid directly above me. I looked at the clock and discovered I had slept for more than two hours, I attributed it to the fact that possibly, because I had not slept the night before. I sat up, readjusted myself and went into the kitchen.

The table was beautifully and colorfully set. Roxanne had picked fresh vegetables and herbs from her garden and made a massive, bountiful, beautiful salad. Edible flowers were throughout the salad. Eating flowers had not been an experience of mine. There was an uncut loaf of very dark bread and a bowl with soft butter, a pitcher of lemonade and a sweet-potato pie. I had never eaten that kind of bread before. It was Pumpernickel-Rye and very delicious with the butter.

Roxanne told me, "since you will be coming here each day, sit, eat and we could get to know each other better." At that moment, I reflected to myself on her words, I will be coming here each day, but what will I be doing? Mrs. Bruebaker asked if I had enjoyed my nap? I was embarrassed, she assured me that what I did was exactly what was supposed to happen. She handed me an envelope, wished me a pleasant evening and stated she would see me the next day. While awaiting the bus, I opened the envelope to discover twenty dollars. If this job were to continue, I would be earning one hundred dollars a week. I didn't know of any Domestic who was earning that amount of money. Reflecting back, I remember that had been an interestingly, unpredictable day, like no other I had ever undergone.

Mr. Coode's abuse, Anthony's indiscretion and his walking-out on me and Mrs. Coode's suicide had taken me by surprise. Roxanne Bruebaker treating me with such kindness and making me feel welcome in her home were unpredictable occurrences. These events my Grandmother Betty had not prepared me for.

Roxanne never told me a specific time to arrive at her house for work, but I had become so accustomed to leaving my home at a specific time each day, I continued the same daily routine. As the bus reached my old exit, the Domestics I had walked up and down that hill with for those past five and a half years got off looked at me and smiled. We never exchanged words. Angel Harp and the man with the khaki - colored clothes remained on the bus even after I exited. Where did they go and when did they return? This new community where I had begun to work was thirty minutes away from my old job site and still those two people did not get off the bus. Where did they go and when did they return?

Roxanne greeted me with a smile when I arrived the next morning, and suggested I spend some alone, quiet time in the Growth Room. She shared with me that afterwards, perhaps I would want to sit in the garden and allow the sun to assist with the nourishing of my starved soul. Again, I had no idea about her references.

When I told Roxanne, it was not comfortable for me to accept her pay and not do a work exchange, I remember her laughter when she said, "I am not the one who is paying you to work, Byron is. He thinks I need a companion here in this big house during the day. What he does not realize is that I have many, many friends and we socialize often. He has insisted on paying your salary and referred to the bad experience you had been a part of. She handed me a copy of the most recent newspaper with its headline:

Community Leader Takes Her Life. The article went on to explain that Janice Coode was the only daughter of Judge Brunswick. Her husband was Byron Coode, the well-known Financial Advisor for the Governor and other government leaders. She had been under the care of her therapist, Dr. Jules Saticoy. Mrs. Coode had been recognized and honored as volunteer of the year at the Daughters of the American Revolution (DAR) Senior Citizens Center. Every Sunday, Mrs. Coode was always in attendance at the First Lutheran Church, a pillar in our community and will be sorely missed. Funeral Services will be held on Friday morning at Grace Lutheran and interment will follow at Golden Dreams Cemetery.

DARLENE'S AWAKENING

Roxanne Bruebaker explained that Janice and Byron had met while in college. She became pregnant and of course in a community being Christian and with a father who was a judge, she had to get married. She and Byron married immediately. It was later she informed him that she had never been pregnant. His repulsion developed, but his career was on the upswing and there was no way he was going to give up his high five- figure salary. They seemed like a loveable couple in public and everyone congratulated them on their relationship. Their friends and associates admired their closeness and dedication to each other. I was surprised because for five and a half years, I had witnessed their obvious distances. Except for the fact they were in the same house, there was no indication they were married. It was more as if they were roommates sharing a space together. I used to wonder if the Coodes talked to each other when they were alone. The fact that the beds in two separate bedrooms needed to be made each day was perhaps another indicator of the distance they shared.

For weeks, I went to this new employment, even though it wasn't really a job. Each day, I was paid twenty dollars. One afternoon, while we were sitting and eating our lunches, Roxanne inquired as to my age, and was flabbergasted when she discovered I was only twenty-two. Roxanne questioned me about my personal life in ways no one else had ever done. In High School, my typing ability was at the advanced level. The idea of being someone's secretary was a fleeting idea, but I had no idea how it would manifest into something tangible. Roxanne was shocked to learn that I had not made plans for my future. Her concern was such that she took a personal interest in directing me to get more of a focus on my days that lay ahead.

She began to take a personal interest in my existence while she questioned me vigorously each day. Her queries caused me to begin investigating and inquiring more about who was I and what did I want out of life? Answers, observations, confusion, conclusions, and solutions spontaneously began to enter my mind each day. Life had been simple before. There had been no thought to do anything other than housework. Nothing else had ever occurred to me, it was what Mama Betty and most of the Negro women had always done since slavery, unless you were lucky enough to have your very own business.

Before Anthony left, there had always been a possibility in the back regions of my mind of us owning our own café, but he never fully embraced my idea. In addition to his palate pleasing menus, his ability to add grace and aesthetic beauty to complete his handiwork was such an inspiration. I knew if more people were able to experience his creations, he would have been successful. His lack of security became a major obstacle in most of his decision making. At different times before his departure, he would say, "I am a man. I ain't complete." Now as I reflect back, I am convinced that our opening a business together would probably have been a major mistake. I had not considered my tomorrow's plans after Anthony's departure.

A few days later Roxanne showed me catalogs from the local College and suggested I browse through them to see if there were any classes that might be of interest to me. She went back to her studio and I laid under the pyramid and looked through the catalogs. I thought how happy Mama Betty would have been to know that I might go to college. The three classes that interested me were, Sociology, Religious Studies and English. Never had I thought about these particular subjects, but the descriptions were appealing. Two weeks later Mrs. Roxanne Bruebaker drove me to Appleton College where I met with a counselor who directed me on how to register. The Counselor informed me if I had difficulty or any questions their office was open to serve all students. My new life was becoming more and more appealing. I was meeting some White people who were friendly and treated me as if my race was of no concern. When I went into the cafeteria there was a mixture of races sitting together at various tables eating or studying together. The sprinkling of Colored students I had never seen in our Westbrite community, where did they come from? It was revealed later that many were International students.

DARLENE'S AWAKENING

This small college an hour and a half from where I had lived most of my life was as if I had traveled far away from my area. Were there some folks in my community east of the Bailey who had known there was a small integrated college with students of all races and religions in attendance? Just a short distance away from where I had grown up and always lived, I believe there was no awareness such a life was available. The following Tuesday morning, I attended my first classes. Tuesdays and Thursdays, I was at school from 9am until 2:30pm. Mondays, Wednesdays and Fridays I was at Roxanne's house studying.

Roxanne had begun to treat me as if I were her family member. A huge salad and other food was always prepared. She understood my disdain for cooking and informed me of the necessity of healthy, balanced meals. Many times, a very tasty dinner was awaiting my arrival. A surprise package with some new articles of clothing might have been placed on my bed. The clothes were always eye pleasing garments and each time they were my exact size. She had unofficially adopted me.

Some weeks later, she invited me to accompany her to the studio where her exhibit was to be. The four other people who were there to help hang her show were friendly and kind. My recent interactions at school and now at the studio with White people who would be friendly to a Colored person presented unexpected exchanges. All of my life, I had learned about our various differences and grown to accept them. But now in my new life where I was being treated as an equal, gave me many moments to reevaluate. Walking around the studio and for the first time really observing the depth, the volume and the intensity of Roxanne's work triggered me to stop and closely examine her expressions. The detail, the use of color she put onto her paintings was absolutely amazing. To imagine this woman whose small physical appearance was able to create work that was huge, bold, colorful but subtle excited my imagination.

Spending more time at Mrs Bruebaker's or at school had become my new pattern. My life had changed considerably. Thinking about Anthony had become less and less as my life was drastically evolving. Going back and forth on those long bus rides with my eyes closed, I was able to access my Grandmother Betty's face that always seemed lit up with a pleasing smile. Lorna, my sister was curious as to why I was always so busy. She wanted to know where I was and what I was doing. When I informed her that I was taking college classes, she congratulated me and told me I was always smart. She shared that her plan was to one day soon return to school and complete her high-school studies.

DARLENE'S AWAKENING

It was on an ordinary day as I had put my books aside while lying under the pyramid that an awareness in me, I never had never known existed before. I gained a feeling of security, a new knowledge erupted, I could not explain the feeling. My thoughts were rapidly moving, my pulse was quickening, it was similar to a rushing river pouring over the sides, cascading into a waterfall. As I breathed in more and relaxed, I understood some of my many questions. I began to listen more and to my surprise, questions, answers and a special kind of support took control of me. I felt protected in an embrace while a new me sprung forth. A reaction emerged almost as if I were being physically pushed. I had to hold back and gain control, the sensation was unexplainable, I felt a need to throw -up and breathed in slowly to gain control. My stomach was churning, I had to purge. I rushed from the room to find Roxanne. Tears had become torrents representing rushing waters in a river and I needed to be rescued before going downstream. My desire to share with her was paramount. The moment I was in her presence, words poured out almost as if they were controlled by a power other than myself. Even though I knew not to interrupt her when she was painting, a force pushed me to open up, with a burst of energy. I told her about what had happened between Bryon and me. I shouted! "He raped me, many, many times. I became pregnant, I had an abortion, my husband discovered it, and my Anthony left me." Very calmly, she put her brushes down, "what you are doing right now is great. Slow down, take some breaths and let's go and have a warm cup of tea." She squeezed my shoulders and held me. Childhood memories of Mama Betty's embraces stepped forward. I began to feel nurtured, safe and loved. I sat at the table and she made peppermint tea with chamomile. We drank tea and had scones. Scones to Roxanne were referred to as sweet biscuits by my Mama Betty sweet biscuits.

Finally, she said, "tell me about it." I told her about his very strange stare and how creepy it made me feel; about how he forced me to have sex over and over; about how he paid me more than his wife as her Domestic; about Janice discovering us and putting a gun to her head; about how I was so alone; about the fears I had because I did not know what to do. I thanked her for her kindness. I told her I never knew a White person could be so nice to a Negro person." She sat patiently and never interrupted. When I finally stopped talking, she asked, "why did you continue to allow Byron to abuse you?" "I didn't know what else to do." I answered. "I had to have a job to take care of myself. With each episode, I felt dirty and guilty, so much so that it became impossible for me to look at myself in a mirror. Going to school, being involved in discussions, observing and finding new acquaintances, many things are beginning to look differently. I want to thank you so much. "

"Darlene, I want to give you some background information on Byron. We do not have biological blood ties, but I love him as if he had lived in my womb for nine months, as if he were my own flesh and blood. His adoptive mother, Lotty was a Negro Woman who was a good friend of mine. She had worked as a nurse at the clinic where I volunteered. According to Lotty, she was approached by the Administrator and told that the daughter of a high-ranking political leader had become pregnant while fooling around with a mixed Colored boy. If the news ever became public, it would have created the political demise of the family. They needed someone to take the baby and remain secret. There would be a monthly stipend for the upkeep of the child. Lotty agreed to adopt the baby. She named him Byron and raised him as her nephew. She loved that boy with all her heart. There was no confusion about her acceptance of him as her own. She became ill and died when he was ten years old. That was when auntie Roxanne and Uncle Phillip became his legal guardians. He is my nephew and I love him very much.

Byron went away to college, and later got married. I never accepted the fact that he married Janice, because I knew of her background and the racial bigotry her family represented. I was concerned about his safety for if Janice's family would have discovered his Negro ancestry. Janice's father was referred to as the "hanging judge," because of the large number of Colored men he had sentenced to hang. I have thought about how it must have felt for Byron when derogatory racial expletives were released as they all sat together having Thanksgiving Dinner or at some other family occasion. In spite of my personal attitude, I was respectful, kind and never let Byron be aware of my true feelings for his wife and her family. His happiness was what mattered to me. Our relationship has always been close. He comes here at least three times a week to be assured that all is well with me.

She was horrified, and very agitated to hear my story of his abuse and did not in any way minimize the experience. She told me that recently she had begun to question him about his dedicated financial support of me. He told her because I was a witness to his wife's suicide, he felt a strong obligation to me. Roxanne had not questioned him further, but she had not totally accepted his account.

Roxanne asked me about my husband. As I reported my memories, I began to realize how I had brushed aside Anthony's dismissal of me even before the abortion. I was still slightly holding on to an unreal past romantic reality that had vanished into the ethers. It was only real to me and not to my husband. A momentary smell of artificial Gardenias penetrated my senses as I was recollecting the past. Remembering that it was Anthony whose impatience with me and his questioning of my dedication to the church doctrine caused me to have some religious doubts. Since I was a child, blindly and without investigation, acceptance of whatever I was told in church was my norm.

It was revealed when I was becoming more familiar with myself that I discontinued going to Sunday Church Services. There were too many contradictions and some statements no longer made sense to me, so many statements the minister made I questioned and disagreed with. A particular memory focused on the minister's statement that God was a jealous God. Those words had always been confusing and frustrating. Why would an all- powerful God who was Omnipresent, Omniscient, Omnipotent have to be jealous about anything? Later, in some of the religious studies classes I was taking at the college and the questions that were being put forth by other students, reminded me again of Anthony and his many religious doubts. In my classes there were vigorous debates and discussions by students who were agnostic, atheist, Christians, Buddhist, Jewish and Moslems. Having been exposed to many different religious philosophies has given me a more specific and a personal understanding of my special connection to that which I refer to as the Source.

Seventh Chapter

EXPLORATION INTO NEW AWARENESS

A NEW DIRECTION

The more I accessed the Pyramid, focused relaxation, stillness, and dedicated listening were skills I became more aware of. By allowing my body and my mind to surrender without expectations, a new self-awareness had sprung forth.

This new approach to myself assisted me in the learning of acceptance and the offering of forgiveness by being willing to ask questions and not to blindly follow along because of an acceptable norm. As I examined the ramifications of this new information, I realized in order for me to move forward I had to forgive.

Forgiving myself for any hurt I had caused myself and others forced me to self-evaluate more objectively the unjustified fears I had held onto based on my lack of knowledge. I studied and became familiar with those ideas that had appeared real to me, and my willingness to accept viewpoints of others because I was unwilling to appreciate the value of my own opinions.

Anthony's constant interrogations forced me to examine preconceived acceptable notions and not blindly follow the popular dictates. A broader appreciation and a treasured realization became some of the acquired benefits. I forgave him for his indiscretions and mentally thanked him for the ways in which I was able to grow as a result of his probing; his questions; his awareness; his stubbornness; and his kindness when he was happy and relaxed. My gratitude for his approach has helped propel me to be more objective in my self-awareness. He was my first real love and his inability to feel complete used to bring sadness when I remembered how talented he was. My ex-husband's lack of self- love prompted me to send loving thoughts to him whenever he was remembered.

DARLENE'S AWAKENING

Janice Coode who treated me as if I were invisible, as if I were not human had taught me that my inability to change others is not my responsibility. From what I had grown to recognize, her upbringing had been as a spoiled child who was taught to feel privileged. In her life, she had been taught that certain races of people were thought to be less. There was no awareness for her to feel guilt in the way she treated me. Based on her training, there were people, usually Negroes, Mexicans and Orientals who were not at the same level and whose only purpose was to serve. From her perspective there was no such thing as exploitation because those workers were lucky to have been hired to help elevate a superior race of people. Forgiving Janice and others, paved the way for me to accelerate in my growth, to become a fully recognized person and to have more self-love.

Forgiving Byron Coode who had assumed the role as my benefactor. I was forced to re-examine my participation in the relationship. My fear and lack of self-worth had led me to have a continual non-participatory sexual relationship for more than a year with Mr. Coode. I questioned my objectives. Had I so easily succumbed after the initial encounters because of the money I was earning, was it because of my husband's distance, was it because on a deeper level I wanted to hurt his wife, was it because somewhere in my unconscious understanding I was enjoying the attention? All these considerations had been visited many times, but now reflecting deeply on my involvement, perhaps I was not as innocent as I had wanted to believe. The victim's role had been accepted by me and any degree of power I might have had was tossed away.

I have forgiven myself for unconscious acts that might have adversely affected others as a result of my lack of perception. Accepting the realization that the only person I may be able to change is myself. The choices I have made, have been based on my conscious or unconscious decisions. Each of us has an innate ability to be different if we so choose. Classes I have been attending since entering Appleton have helped me to understand the concept that no one has the capacity at a given moment to be any more than they are. An objective awareness of self must be recognized and accepted in order for a real change to manifest.

Recognizing, accepting responsibility and knowing the decisions I had made had been based on my thoughts, words, and actions. Blaming others for my happiness or unhappiness was not justified. My lack of experience and exposure blocked my expanse, but thankfully new opportunities have been given. Because of the constant awareness of forgiving myself and others that concept has permitted me to forge ahead in my search for true happiness.

I began to understand and appreciate Roxanne's suggestions when she directed me to just lie still and listen.

Lying under the pyramid a never before experienced force was manifested; questions, answers and ideas were free flowing. Sometimes the information was appearing much faster than I was able to comprehend. But on this day, I knew that I must no longer allow my life to just "pass by."

Byron knew not to visit his aunt during those times I was at the house and I respected him for maintaining a distance when I was there. In keeping with the continuous unraveling of my life, observing the unpredictable course it had taken, I had become more aware as to how his aggression, had directed and assisted me in finding myself; had forced me to probe deeper into a more definitive introspection as I asked the question, who am I?

At the insistence of Roxanne, I agreed to move into her house. My fourth quarter at college I moved into a new home and gave ownership of my Grandmother's home to my sister Lorna. Moving to this new location was much more convenient for my travels back and forth to school. Roxanne was an easy roommate without demands. She encouraged me and treated me as if I were her relative.

DARLENE'S AWAKENING

Fortunately, because reading was one of my joys, the new information I was acquiring was stimulating and captivating. My studies had become my priority. Days and nights were occupied with writing, reading, researching and study group involvement. Going to school had been an important substitute for the sadness and confusion that had been generated in my life. However, the impact of those circumstances forced a conscious transition. Each quarter, I had made the Dean's list with a steady 4.0 GPA. Sociology, Psychology, Human Concerns, and Comparative Religions exposed me to concepts I may have taken for granted; however, the more I have studied these seemingly new ideas I have begun to know that somewhere embedded in the chambers of my mind, I had already understood. The notions of respect and justice for everyone, the importance of good communication and many other thoughts rose to the surface of my awareness.

In my particularly stimulating and thought-provoking sociology class. the professor encouraged and permitted discussions. On a particular day as students entered the room, sprawled across the board in large letters was written, the name, Martin Luther King, the Negro minister who was becoming more familiar. This was to be the main topic of discussion. His name generated strong opinions. One very disgruntled, white, female student yelled out, "why can't they stay on the other side of the BAILEY?" Two other students and I were the only Coloreds in the class and before we were able to respond another White female student shouted, " that doesn't make sense, what does that have to do with our discussion? It's Racist like you that stop society from going forward. From those comments a huge debate ensued. The professor facilitated by asking many questions, writing quotations on the board, presenting historical and current facts while allowing students to present their own personal opinions.

After a lengthy debate, Professor Wells interrupted. "We can continue this at our next session. In addition to what is listed on your class syllabus, three pages, double- spaced evaluating today's discussion should be submitted at our next gathering. Thank you for today's class."

The topic had drawn so much interest, that agitated, concerned, probing, energy was released in the cafeteria at lunch time. Students who had not attended the class became involved. I spoke up when a reference was made that no Whites lived east of the BAILEY. "That's not true, the Boticellis and several other white families I have known all of my life are my neighbors. We have lived side by side forever with no animosity." "Boticelli, that is not a surname for a White person," a male White student laughed as he commented.

Later that evening, as Roxanne and I were discussing the day while having our ritualistic cup of tea, I told her about the vociferous exchanges between the students where opinions and facts were being shared. She voiced, "those were some of the very good benefits of college. Some students get to hear information and form new values and ideas based on these exchanges." "Why was the name Boticelli referred to as a nonwhite name? What was the problem with it, I wanted to know?" She answered, "sometimes people have limited perceptions about who is acceptable and who is not. Some Europeans in the more Eastern countries and those from Southern Europe are not considered as equal to those in many of the more northern areas. I have visited countless countries and the segregated racial, divide exists almost everywhere. The Japanese and the Okinawans who look very similar, in India there were the so- called Untouchables. There is a division in groups who share the same ethnicity based on skin color, or religion or some other nonsense. Darlene I could cite examples all around the world. I believe when people can truthfully and unequivocally love and forgive themselves, and do the same with others, we could have the perfect place. I know, even at my age, I am very idealistic, and I am pleased to have been able to hold on to my ideals. Ignorance has been a key factor in keeping people segregated.

Insecurity, unrealistic fears, a false sense of superiority have produced citizens who do not recognize the Oneness of all. Appreciating the contributions of others, realizing how learning is constant and lessons acquired with each encounter demonstrate wisdom. It is not necessary to look the same or have the same ideas, respecting others is a key component in the happiness for all citizens. I am so happy for you to be able to be in a class where you are forced to think and to ask questions and pose solutions. You have been meeting people who have come from places very far away and some from areas close by. I salute you for the manner in which you have become dedicated to your commitment to improving yourself. "

As usual Roxanne offered such wisdom, she got up, kissed me on the forehead and exited the room. I realized, we share a special heart connection and because of that our racial differences are of no concern. I really love and appreciate my new family member.

At Appleton College, the recent friends in my various study groups helped to increase my understanding of different cultures and religions. What impressed me the most was the fact that approximately an hour and a half away eastward across the BAILEY, there were people who were still living as their ancestors had decades ago. After yesterday's class discussion, I knew there were some residents west of the BAILEY who were happy things had always stayed the way they were and some east of the BAILEY who had no clue that other options were available. I wondered how Anthony might have functioned in this multi-cultural environment, where many were aware and appreciated their heritage but were also able to embrace and respect others.

Under a bright, cloudless, perfect, blue-sky day while rushing across campus to last afternoon next class, I almost bumped into Byron Coode. He was as surprised as I. He excused himself from the person who had been accompanying him and asked if we could have a brief conversation. I reluctantly agreed. Almost a year and a half had passed since we had last seen each other. Our eyes met and I didn't get the strange eerie feeling I used to experience when I would see the way in which he stared at me. It was the first time we had actually looked directly at each other; it was the first time I felt no discomfort from the closeness of our encounter; it was the first time I felt in complete control of my senses. I observed my body and felt strongly rooted.

"Please accept my most heartfelt apology. It has been very burdensome for me as I realize how I must have hurt you. I am in therapy and I have come to realize my intentions were those of a bully. Please, please forgive me I am so sorry." Tears were running down on his face when he took out a handkerchief and began to wipe them away. He was still in the middle of his dialog when I interrupted and said, "I forgive you Mr. Coode, I must go now or I will be late to my class." As I was rushing to get away from this very dumbfounding meeting, he said," please call me Byron, not Mr. Coode."

Focusing on the lectures being given in each of my classes the remainder of the day was almost impossible. All of my attempts to stay focused were in vain.

Anxious to share with Roxanne my day's interaction with Mr. Coode, I rushed home from my last class. She listened patiently and when I was finished, she inquired about my emotional state. I assured her that I was okay, but the shock of seeing him for the first time after such a long interval had left me a bit ill at ease. When I first saw him, my knees were unstable, but immediately I grabbed hold to me and steadied myself. Perhaps, the encounter had more of an impact than I was aware of because I barely remembered the details of any of my classes.

DARLENE'S AWAKENING

Roxanne said, "Byron called this afternoon and informed me that he was so shaken from bumping into you that he cancelled all of his regular appointments. He told me he had seen you at different times on the campus, and at each possible confrontation, he made countless efforts to avoid your running into each other. He told me that he had been in therapy several times a week, an activity I had been unaware of.

I said to him, "It was an absolutely horrible, disgusting thing you did. You violated an unsuspecting, confused woman who you took advantage of. You are fortunate that Darlene is such an exceptional person. Your suffering, you have caused to yourself. Now you are being forced to face the consequences of your actions." It was the first time I had addressed the issue with him. He was so embarrassed because of his past actions with you and also the fact that I was privy to the information. He continued to ask me what he should do. I suggested whenever it became possible for him to use the Growth Room and allow his common sense and a sense of decency to provide him the solutions he was looking for."

Lorna and her family had been to visit me a few times at my new home. At their first encounter with Roxanne, immediately they all bonded in a loving way. It was also Lorna and her family's first time to connect with a White person on a personal level. Racial separation was non-existent. An unspoken realization of our Oneness overtook those things that compete with the beauty we all have to give.

At the very first meeting, Roxanne became Grandmother to Lorna and Larcel's four offspring. She expressed how she had longed to have grandchildren. Without hesitation, the youngsters accepted their new Grandmother and had to be gently corralled in order to learn the perimeters of the new environment. The kids especially enjoyed the swimming hole down below the house where other children congregated and swam. Larcel, Lorna's husband spent much time in the Growth Room and according to him, his inability to share the feelings he experienced was because there were no adequate words to express what he had felt. Larcel stated, "the insides of my body from my head to my feet is singing and dancin like they celebratin, seems like my brain was washed. I don know how to talk bout it, but it's good." According to him, never in his life had something so mysterious, so strange produced such a good feeling. He felt as if all troubles went awa and happiness and joy overtook his body each time he sat in that room.

Roxanne understood his reactions perfectly and explained those were some of the sensations she first experienced at a retreat high up in the mountains of Katmandu on the slopes of the Himalayas. At first, she thought perhaps the geographical location and the extremely high altitude were the main determiners of the delight that had burst forth as she laid under a pyramid. However, once a device was installed in her house, that unexplainable joy in her body again manifested; solutions to confusing situations provided more clarity. Roxanne realized the value of this rare apparatus. All of the people with whom she had known who had been associated with the very particular type of pyramid installation had since disappeared from her life, and as a result, there was no data giving information where others might be attained.

Listening to Roxanne share some details about her world travels with us always took priority over whatever else we might have been doing. Numerous times I wished Grandmother Betty would have been present. The way in which my life had transformed in these past few years was more than remarkable.

DARLENE'S AWAKENING

On a quiet, undemanding day while sitting in the garden, enveloped in the perfect temperature of the sun's illumination, absorbing the perfection of the natural order, accepting the radiance, observing the bees pollinating while perpetuating continuity and relaxing from my studies, I decided to call Priscilla, my ex sister-in-law. We had developed a close relationship when her brother, Anthony and I were married. The two of us had not spoken since his departure approximately four years ago. The minute she answered the phone and heard my voice, I detected an unfriendly attitude. Her response to me was, "how dare you have the nerve to call here after the way you cheated on my brother. Have you no shame? What kind of person are you anyway to have gotten pregnant by someone else when Anthony loved you so much?

My brother is happily married again, and they have two children." Her announcement dismantled me for a moment. My response was," I am happy for him." Though, I wondered how he was able to have children. The information I remembered was that he was sterile. My assumption was that his new wife must have had children when they got married. Anthony had been such a quitter during our time together. I hoped for the children's emotional stability, he would remain in their lives and not abandon them as their attachment became stronger. At any rate as I was pondering the situation, and before I had an opportunity to inquire more, my thoughts were interrupted by her very unfriendly response. "You should be ashamed of yourself and how did you have the nerve to call me?" She raised her voice and told me to lose her phone number and to never, ever in this life call her again.

Priscilla's pejorative reaction surprised me because I had thought we shared a sisterly closeness. Her attitude was the same as her brother's the night we had our blowup and he walked out of my life. She did not ask me for an explanation and expressed no care or concern for what might have happened to me. Her judgement was based entirely on her brother's subjective report. I wondered if he had shared with her the putrid, artificial gardenia smell on his garments, the lipstick on his shirt and the indiscretions he had participated in.

In the past few years, my life had been disassembled by unexpected changes so many times, that her reaction was an additional adjustment. To say I was hurt and shaken was an understatement. Observing and realizing my ability to remain in control of my feelings and to not be reactive was a step in a more secure acceptance of myself. Priscilla's unkind attitude may have caused me much consternation in the past, but as the saying goes, "my skin has become a bit tougher." The growth and development I have been experiencing since moving from my very familiar environment has been more than incredible. Receiving love from and returning it to Roxanne, my new family member, a White woman; divorcing Anthony who had not been able to fully accept himself; entering college, a very distinct contrast from my life East of the BAILEY, accessing topics and people from all over the world has introduced Me to Me in ways never before realized. I like the new Me. I feel more comfortable to question and realize we may not always agree with each other, but respect is essential. The role of a frightened, young, Colored girl has vanished. The options that are provided have to do with our acceptance or non- acceptance of other people's judgments. Do we react or become non-reactive to comments and attitudes from others? Becoming more aware of the value of not permitting others to define my happiness has given me a broader insight into being my true self.

I hung up the phone, breathed in slowly, regained my composure and knew that chapter in my life had totally and completely come to an end and still I sent loving thoughts to Anthony and his new family.

DARLENE'S AWAKENING

The following weekend, Arriving at Roxanne's latest Art Opening, "The Ocean and Its Environment," was the title that greeted guests at the entrance. Lorna had accompanied me and when I looked at her, it was if her eyes were bulging out of their sockets. Generally, she had much to say; however, my sister remained totally quiet and walked away from me awestruck. I heard her say, "Larcel and the kids have got to see this, it is unbelievable." There was an illusion of walking under water. Pieces were hanging from the ceiling representing seaweed and other creatures. She had been able with proper shading and color infusion to bring light to darker places that resembled caves underwater. Some of the lighter areas depicted Coral reefs that looked unbelievably real. I was reminded of the actual ones I had seen in a Marine Biology class. All of the rooms in this exhibit were painted in blues, turquoises with shades of green. The individual paintings on the walls depicted sharks, octopuses, dolphins, turtles, fish of various descriptions and an assortment representing flora and fauna of undersea life, many I hadn't seen before. The most impressive painting as one entered the largest room was that of a huge, monster sized whale covering most of the wall.

Roxanne's ability to combine colors, be responsible for each detail, and have works that were so expressive created a curious longing in my being that was hungry for more. I had been to the river in our community and a few times to the lake but had only seen the ocean in books or the movies, so I was most impressed. As I walked through the exhibit, people were making comments about how mesmerized they were. Some were exclaiming they had never witnessed an exhibit with such realism. Roxanne shared,she had been approached by an art museum that was interested in installing the show as a permanent display. Her paintings inspired me to such a degree, I knew at some future time I would have to have first -hand knowledge of the ocean as it had been related to me. I looked forward to an experience that would allow the sand to engulf and massage my feet, to lie flat on my back and inhale and exhale with the rhythm and movement of the waves; to watch the evening's sun as it disappeared into the sea. Those were some of the highlights of being at the ocean's edge she had told me about. I was looking forward to times in the future when I would have similar familiarity.

It was when I had become so involved in my appreciation of Roxanne's works that I heard Lorna ask, " Darlene who is that man and why is he staring so hard at you? I looked in the direction she was referring to and there he was, Mr. Coode, Byron. Our eyes met and he approached me. When he was within range, he greeted me and asked, "who is the attractive woman standing next to you?" "She is my sister." I introduced the two of them. The astonishment of seeing him and thinking about what must have been in Lorna's mind created such a shock that I became lost in a moment of confusion. Before time was allowed for me to say anything else, he said," May I have a private moment with you, there is something important I need to share? " I looked at Lorna as she raised her eyebrow. A recognizable mannerism she displayed when puzzling inquiries were presented to her. I nodded my head in agreement to his invitation and he and I exited to the patio.

As soon as we were at a private place, he blurted out, "I purposely came today, because I knew you would be here. Ever since we encountered each other on campus a few weeks ago, I cannot get you out of my mind. I love you very much and I want to spend the rest of my life with you if you will have me." "Mr. Coode, what have you been drinking?" That was the best response I was able to bring forth at the moment.

"Please do not call me Mr. Coode, please call me Byron. I have loved you even before you arrived at my home as a Domestic. For years you appeared in my dreams. When I first saw you, I couldn't believe you were the exact person who I had dreamed about. I stared at you in disbelief because of those recollections, you are the one I have been waiting for. It has been impossible for me to clear my mind of you. When I shared my dilemma with my therapist, it was suggested I tell you and that is what I have done today. I love you very much."

My legs had turned to a gelatinous substance, the bones had vanished, there was no support., It was as if I were being controlled by some force I couldn't identify. I grabbed hold to the wall. The words I had wanted to express had lost their way, my tongue was glued to the roof of my mouth, my teeth were grinding together. All I was able to do was stare.

"Are you okay, I have never wanted to hurt you. I do not wish to cause you harm or any degree of unhappiness. If you give me a chance, I am certain we can become close. You will learn to love me. You do not need to answer me at this time. May I please call on you and take you to dinner or a movie or just a walk in the park or anything you may want to do? Do you understand? You look absolutely stunning. I want to spend the rest of my life with you," he repeated.

My words had found their way back, "yes, I hear you." Did he really say what I thought he had said? Possibly, I was confused. My judgments were obscured in a cloud of uncertainty. Perhaps, he had drunk too many of the glasses of wine that had been circulating. Had he become mentally deficient? What was the matter with this man? Unaware as to how to respond logically I answered, "Please excuse me, I need to find the ladies' room." I rushed to the restroom with Lorna in close pursuit. Once we entered, she could barely hold her enthusiasm, "that was him, your ex-boss and what did he want?" I realized I had never told her about the encounter he and I had had on campus a several weeks ago. Just as I was about to explain, Roxanne entered. "Is everything okay? What did Byron say to you? Was he respectful and kind?"

"That was Byron, Mr. Coode," Lorna asked? Both of them were looking at me and talking so fast, I just needed time to collect myself again. "He told me he loved me very much and wanted to spend the rest of his life with me." Roxanne in her usual, very patient way said,

" are you enjoying my show? Relax and listen to yourself. You do not need to make decisions now. We will talk later." With those words, she went back to her guest. Lorna had a million questions? Is he ??? Oh my goodness! Was that him? He's a looker. What did you tell him? He said he wanted to marry you and spend the rest of his life with you, really. Wow, Darlene, what are you going to do? Do you like him? Wow, Darlene!" I had no idea how I was to be at that precise moment. The exhibit was a perfect metaphor, I was lost at sea reaching for the rudder, looking for dry land, reaching for an anchor. I needed to grab hold before everything was lost. I knew once I exited the powder room, he would be waiting. My emotions were in chaos, as I once again and very slowly re-entered the main room, he was nowhere to be seen, apparently, he had left. Lorna continued to question me, but I had no response. So confused was I, there were no easy answers. Glances were exchanged between Roxanne and me. She smiled, I do not remember my expression, I suppose it must have been one of bewilderment.

Once I returned home from the exhibit, I had allowed myself the opportunity to enter the Growth Room for some of the confusion that had manifested to become clearer. Each instance as I sat and awaited clarity, nothing came forth.

Roxanne and I had not spoken about the incident, but I was certain she was waiting for a response from me as to my intentions. I had no answers, that feeling which had appeared in the past was there again, it was as if I were hanging on a ledge awaiting to be rescued but was left there alone to try and figure how to save myself. "Roxanne, I have no answer, I do not know how to respond to Byron. Never had I considered he might have had the feelings he expressed. The question of my loving him or having any kind of exchange with him had never been a consideration. What am I to do?"

"There is nothing for you to do but to continue with your life, give yourself permission to accept the quietness whenever the moments are available. Use the Growth Room incessantly and answers you are looking for will avail themselves to you. Your patience and calmness will guide you to the answers you are requiring."

DARLENE'S AWAKENING

The following day when I arrived home from school, there was a long-stemmed red rose with an attached note stating, I love you very much, please consider being my wife and sharing the rest of your life with me. I am positive we can be happy together." Roxanne had seen it before I came home and questioned me about my encounter with Byron the day before at her exhibit. I was still very perplexed. I had forgiven him for his aggression some time ago, but never had I considered the fact of him expressing his love for me and suggesting that we marry and spend the rest of our lives together.

She told me the amount of work that had been involved in putting her show together for yesterday's opening had required an inordinate amount of dedication and she was physically exhausted; therefore, she was going away to a Spa for the next ten days. My immediate thought was, I was going to be alone and I hoped Byron would not ignore my need for privacy.

For the next ten days after Roxanne left, I continued going to school each day. Byron did not come to the house when I was there but most days, there were reminders of his presence; sometimes, a huge bouquet of flowers with accompanying notes expressing his love for me was left on the kitchen table. On one of those days a beautiful hand painted silk scarf in a matching box was perfectly positioned. Another day there was a delicately designed gold necklace with letters spelling out my name, and the gift that melted my heart was a picture of Grandma Betty in a hand-carved frame with a note attached that read, she would have loved me and would have wanted the two of us to spend our lives together. Where and how did he acquire a photo of Mama Betty? Each of the ten days Roxanne was away at her retreat, there was either a gift with a note at the front entrance to the house or on the kitchen table.

Roxanne returned and looked extremely relaxed with a glow I had not previously observed before her departure. She questioned me about my times when she was away. I showed her the gifts and messages expressing love Byron had left each day. I told her how the framed photograph of my Grandmother had taken me to a place I was unprepared for. At that point Roxanne remembered he had asked her for Lorna's telephone number. He must have gotten information from Lorna. She wanted to know if he had come to the house and disturbed me. I told her definitely not and that I had never seen him. She also inquired if I had come to a resolution regarding his advances. Observing myself, I realized many of my thoughts were concerning him, but nothing definitive had erupted.

Eighth Chapter

THINGS CHANGE....

THINGS REMAIN THE SAME

PATIENCE......KINDNESS

Lorna called to inform me that Mr. Williams had died and his memorial services would be held on the following Saturday. She invited me to accompany her. Usually, I steered clear of funerals, but the memories of Mr. Williams sitting on his porch, sharing about his deceased wife's unhealthy eating habits and always offering advice brought back memories I didn't want to let go of. The last time we had interacted was when he told me what a "good girl" I was and if I ever needed anything, he would be there to help me. Friday afternoon, I boarded the bus and rode to my old neighborhood where I would spend the weekend with my sister and her family. For almost two and a half years I had lived at Roxanne's house, and nothing in my old neighborhood had changed. As I exited the bus and walked down that familiar sidewalk, there was Barlo, looking through the fence and barking loudly. His bark was so loud and so agitated that Mr. Boticelli came out to understand why the dog was making such a racket. When I got closer, Barlo was running back and forth along the fence. Mr. Boticelli informed me that each day at a given time Barlo would look through the fence as the bus stopped. On this day, he was behaving in a way he never had before. I explained I had been going to college and had moved a distance away. I inquired as to if I would be able to sit with Barlo for a few minutes. Rooting myself comfortably on the ground, Barlo nudged against me. It was the first time we had a physical encounter. He rubbed his head against me as I stroked him. Most of the Boticelli family had emerged from the house and were amazed at the relationship between Barlo and me. He was almost burying his head on my shoulder. The emotional experience between the dog and me was one I will always remember. As I got up to leave, he let out a howl as if he were crying. It was a most unusual experience. I left his yard and we walked parallel to each other as we had done on previous afternoons with the cyclone fence separating us. I uttered my familiar, "see you later Barlo." and continued to Lorna's.

DARLENE'S AWAKENING

When I first got off the bus, nothing appeared to have changed, but the more I observed, the more I realized subtle changes had taken place. Across the street, Mrs. Wilson's hydrangea plants looked much healthier than before. The colors of the flowers were more intense than they had been when I used to see them each day. Looking at her yard, I realized I must visit her before I returned home, she and my Grandmother had been very good church acquaintances.

Strolling along on the sidewalk, I reached Mr. Williams' home. His empty chair looked very inappropriate, remaining there by itself. When having conversation with him, it was difficult to see the separation between the two. He and his chair had melded, they had become fused into one. As I looked at this porch, it was very unfamiliar, I realized I had never seen it before because when you were engaged with Mr. William, he was the center, and the surroundings were insignificant.

Probably neighbors and friends would have colorful reflections about him sitting on the porch sharing tales and reminiscing about his dead wife as they passed his house. Mr. Williams' absence from the confines of his front porch must have been a big loss for the people who walked back and forth past his home. Because of the location of his home, there was a constant foot traffic of the passersby. He knew all of them and retold his story many times to those he could capture. There were some of us who knew to speak and continue our walk because if you paused for a brief time, you would be confined in his embrace with accounts of his past activities. Listening to Mr. Williams as he revealed segments about some of his past experiences, captured me multiple times. My familiarity with those repeated tales helped me develop patience. So many times, I became locked in his chamber and no escape route was apparent.

Would he and his wife, Letty whom he spoke so lovingly about reunite? If the bodies are decaying in a casket, then what goes to Heaven or Hell? I had no answer, but there was an unexplainable curiosity jarring me. My college classes have helped to unleash, release, open-up, examine such concerns and still I have no satisfactory answers. I know what it is I know, but there are not always words to describe those understandings stored in my reservoirs. That was the question I pondered as I passed his home. My curiosity took me to a place where I wondered if the two of them would connect again?

At Mrs. Jones's home directly next door to Lorna's, there was a huge for sale sign posted. My sister reported that our local seamstress and her four employees had been hired to sew for some famous designer. She and her crew were moving to the big city.

Entering the house and looking around at the changes Lorna and Larcel had made offered a pleasant surprise. Most of the furniture had been removed. They had donated it to the church for a new Community Center. Other items had been given to a local Y.W.C.A. The transformation was such that I barely recognized some of the areas. Each room had been given fresh paint, the old carpets had been removed to display the beautiful hardwood floors that had been covered over for decades. New lighter curtains donned each window. The house was so altered that memories of Anthony and me having lived there had been removed as the renovation took place.

The brightness coming in through the windows reminded me that in spite of the darkness, the light always returns. Freedom and spring days when all was in bloom and a freshness that could not be dismissed had been invited in. Even the smells pleasantly stimulated my olfactory senses. The appearance of the many changes presented a more welcoming model. It would have been interesting to know our Grandmother's reaction with such a beautiful transformation

DARLENE'S AWAKENING

There used to be a feeling of heaviness in my head which was probably precipitated by the residential fungi. Since childhood, my sneezing had been non-stop at various occasions. It was unexplainable and felt as though I were being held down unable to breathe freely. The mold and mildew that had grown under and around the heaps of furniture and other discards were the initiators of my compromised allergies. The doctor told Mama Betty, not to have much concern because children experience various sensitivities and eventually grow out of them.

Entering this newly transformed house that had been dusted, vacuumed, swept, polished, waxed and sprayed had removed all traces of invasive, and unwelcomed substances. I reflected on the contrast of the old house, its furnishings and the beautiful changes Lorna and Larcel had been responsible for. Being outdoors was always more welcoming than being closed inside the house with too much furniture and other things. The new transformation of the interior was much more pleasant. The appearance of the many changes presented a more welcoming model. It would have been interesting to know our Grandmother's reaction with such a beautiful transformation.

I relaxed, settled in, played games, answered millions of questions from my nieces and nephews. Later in the evening, when the kids had gone to bed and Lorna and I were cleaning the kitchen I was able to get my sister's undivided attention. I asked her if she had been talking to Byron. She laughed and teased me by referring to him as Byron instead of Mr. Coode. I replied, "that's his name and he has asked me not to call him Mr. Coode. You are so crazy Lorna Mae."

"Yeah, I am crazy," she responded, "just like a fox." She was laughing while speaking, her laughter was such that most of what she was saying was undecipherable. Finally, she gained her composure and told me they had had several conversations. "He really cares for you Darlene. I believe he is sincere and genuine; I believe deep down he really cares for you. He told Larcel and me about how you were in his dreams before you ever began to work in his home. He is not like my ex-boss who took advantage of me. Byron is so embarrassed and wants to care for you. The photo of Mama Betty that he had reproduced and framed was his idea. He has visited us a few times and my kids like him also."

Saturday morning, I walked to the market and said hello to the Chows. They wanted to know where I had been and when I told them I was a college student. They were shocked and so happy. Mrs. Chow called all the family to have a photo taken with me. As I was leaving, we all hugged, l they wished me good luck and gave me a box of Chinese Fortune Cookies

DARLENE'S AWAKENING

I crossed the street to visit Mrs. Wilson who appeared to be in very good health. She seemed unable to maintain her curiosity about my whereabouts for the past two and a half years. I explained to her and shared some of my experiences as a college student. Like the other neighbors I had shared my new life with, she too was overly excited. She escorted me to the back of her house, an area I had never seen before. Her garden was immense with beautiful, healthy looking flowers, fruits and vegetables. Strawberries were in profusion, lettuce, tomatoes, varieties of peppers, string beans trailing up the corn, squash, peas and different herbs. I had stepped into what seemed like a mysterious domain where, the insects, the flowers and vegetables gave me the impression they were smiling and vibrating at a rapid frequency. Perching birds, eating, singing and flitting from their birdhouses to overhanging tree- branches while dancing to their own rhythms. The multi-colored flowers attracted bees who were performing their rhythmic ritual. I knew the importance of their activities and felt gratitude. Was it my imagination as I viewed some of the plants or were they actually smiling and expressing contentment? There was a light breeze blowing fragrances enveloping all parts of my body. Spending multiple hours in this little plot of sustenance, an environment that offered peace, tranquility and freshness offered a perspective as to why Mrs. Wislon always looked so healthy, so relaxed, so refreshed, so energized and so wrinkle free at her advancing age. As I observed her more closely, I noticed the texture of her almost flawless skin.

She then escorted me to her front yard where for the first time, I was able to get a closer look at her Hydrangea plants. They were enormous and offered an eye warming vision. During the period of my absence, the bushes had been thinned- out and since that time, their roots had more room to expand, thus allowing each flower to become larger, with more intense hues.

Happily, I received the beautiful assortment of fresh produce Mrs. Wilson had gathered and bagged for me. She smiled as she said," your grandmother would have been so proud of you. I remember when she shared your high-school diploma and now you are a college student. I am happy for you. Please come and visit whenever you are in the neighborhood." We embraced, and I walked back to Lorna's. These were happy times as I visited my old neighborhood.

Later that day, I attended Mr.Williams' funeral and just like all the others I had attended, the sadness was the overriding sentiment. I do understand sadness or emptiness that is experienced as we lose a relative, friend or anyone. Are there other options? Is it really the end and if so, the end of what, maybe the end of life for a while on this planet? Does it mean we are born; we die, we do the work and then we are tossed to oblivion? There are religions that embrace reincarnation with an understanding that the life cycle on earth continues again and again until a higher state of consciousness has been realized. Some religious or spiritual philosophies joyfully celebrate the person's life at funeral ceremonies. Realizing and recognizing there are many approaches to the celebration of life and death, I have learned to appreciate the uniqueness of the various attitudes. Changes in my perceptions of differing thoughts has become accepted. It is as if each day new information has penetrated my existence. Questions and more questions that were hanging out on the fringes of my awareness have eased. Fortunately, the Growth Room has been available for my use. Learning to be quiet while refining my listening has helped me to grow in ways that enhance my continuity.

DARLENE'S AWAKENING

Mr. Williams' ceremony did not reflect the man I had spent years listening to or laughing with as he would provide his daily assessments while observing the people going back and forth. The funeral was heavy with most people wearing black, navy blue or brown with such a degree of finality. The music was sad and slow. Mr. Williams loved to laugh and joke as he shared his tales. There was no reference about the joy of life, no reference about life being eternal, no references for the possibility that once we become devoid of our physical encumbrances, the soul or the spirit continues. The service focused on The Journey's End. At the end of the Service as cars were lining up to go to the graveyard, I declined and decided I had paid my respects and headed back home. That was enough sadness for one day. Since I had taken Comparative Religion courses, and with my ex-husband's inquiries, my spiritual awareness had become somewhat different from those religious values I had grown up accepting and being accustomed to.

Sunday morning, I respectfully declined Lorna and her family's invitation to accompany them to church. The children reminded me of my past self, innocently accepting doctrine without question. Hopefully, my nieces and nephews would become curious enough to investigate some of the teachings before they reached adult age. The family was perfectly adorned in their Sunday attire as they all left.

In the quietness of the morning, I studied and completed some assignments that needed my attention. At last, the kitchen was cleaned, everything was in order when I decided to venture to the attic. It had been a long while since I had entered that room. A surprise awaited me as I pushed open the door. There was order and organization from one wall to the other. The ghosts who may have lived there in the past had been evicted. No dark corners inhabited by Daddy Long Legs; no windows covered with grime and vines. The attic had become a welcoming and a comfortable place for seclusion. One of the few remaining memories from the past were my three boxes of neatly stacked books. Opening the box labeled Negroes, the first book on the top was one written about Phyllis Wheatley and her poetry. Stretching out on the pillows that had been carefully arranged on the carpet provided me a momentary escape as I dove into some of the history of this remarkable ex-slave woman.

Comfortably, surrendering for the very first time in the attic's new arrangement, I reflected on Anthony's Sunday afternoon dinners when I used to return home from church, where a surprising menu was in the offering and the house was in order. Seeping thoughts of Byron Coode and the strange relationship that was developing crept in. The new configuration of the attic compared to what it had become and what it used to be provided a metaphorical moment when I thought of the contrast between these two strikingly dissimilar men.

Returning to the kitchen to get a glass of water, I considered preparing a meal for the family once they returned home. The more I pondered the idea, I realized my disdain for cooking would not have allowed me to prepare anything deliciously memorable. The thought was tossed into oblivion as I drank a glass of water and went outside, to observe the day from a different perspective. Relaxing in the rocking chair on the front porch reminded me of Mama Betty sitting with closed eyes, shoes tossed to the side, humming a favorite hymn. I gained more of an appreciation of the appeal so many neighbors had sitting high above the sidewalk with a degree of privacy, comfort and a more focused view of the neighborhood.

The idea of fixing dinner again pounded my brain and had I been more confident with food preparation, I would have prepared a meal for the family when they returned, but when I looked in the refrigerator again trying to come up with a culinary idea my mind became blank, and I decided to forego the thought.

Lorna and the family had already eaten when they returned and brought me a prepared meal. She who was extremely familiar with my lack of food preparation laughed and expressed her gratitude for me not cooking. In fact we all were laughing at the possibility of what I might have made for Sunday dinner.

DARLENE'S AWAKENING

The following morning, I got up early, we all kissed and hugged. I rushed to catch the bus. I left home fifteen minutes earlier than I used to. Arriving at the bus stop, Miss TGR was already there. She must have wondered about my whereabouts for the past two years. Her curiosity was evident as she began questioning me as soon as I arrived. She told me she had heard that I was doing something remarkable in another town, but she wasn't sure what it was. When I told her I was a college student at Applelton College, she congratulated me and had a multitude of questions. She was still inquiring as the bus pulled up. The most interesting of her interrogations was when she assumed Appleton College was far away. This woman many years my senior had no idea that less than two hours away was a college where Negroes could attend.

Reminiscences of the past erupted as Mrs. Wilson rushed from the back to wave just as she had done in those past years. The same driver, Pete, smiled at me as I boarded for the first time in more than two years. Our morning greetings had always been a brief exchange of typical pleasantries, "good morning." Perhaps because each morning, six other passengers boarded with me there was not the opportunity for more conversation. On that particular morning, the prearranged bus schedule and the number of people who were getting on the bus was not a significant concern to Pete. He took the time and looked directly into my eyes when he asked, "Where have you been? I have wondered about you." "I am a college student and have been attending classes at Appelton." "That is a very good thing you are doing for yourself. It's good to see you. Well, you take care and keep up the good work." He smiled and I chose a seat near the front of the bus. Our talk ended and some of the passengers who had overheard the conversation smiled or winked at me as I found a seat. It was so encouraging to see their non-verbal support. Mrs. TGR must have been informing passengers about my new life. She was whispering and gesturing towards me. In fact, there was a buzz bouncing off the windows to the ceiling down to the floor. Passengers whom I had never had a connection with were winking to me, smiling and just sending joyful support. I felt happy realizing a new chapter had begun and the past chapter had been a good catalyst for my development. As the bus continued along, those same passengers I had grown familiar with two and a half years ago boarded the bus in the exact manner wearing the same attire. There he was, the strange khaki-clad man carrying his identical items that I remembered. Was it a different book, its color looked the same, when did he read? The brown paper bag, and green thermos could have been the exact ones from two years ago, were they? My sense of self has strengthened and no longer was I intimidated by his behavior. I had decided if he sat next to me, I would attempt to engage him in conversation. He saw me and for a very fleeting moment, an almost smile escaped. He chose to sit next to me with no acknowledgement of being present in his body. "Good morning, it's nice to see you again." His response was only a grunt. I had no expectations and was able to relax and silently offer him solace. The odious smell of liniment I remembered was not apparent. In fact he smelled of fresh as if he had rolled in fresh. peppermint

DARLENE'S AWAKENING

I used to close my eyes on those long bus rides, but on this day, they were wide open, I wanted to observe everything and self-evaluate my perceptions. Angel Harp entered the bus and performed the similar ritual I had seen many times. Nothing in her delivery had changed. Who was this mysterious woman, what did she do each day and where did she go? Her attempt was to preach to whomever would listen, encourage the reading of their bibles and remind everybody that God loved them. On this particular Monday morning, she was wearing an amber colored skirt with a blouse made of a yellow, shiny material. The scarf around her neck was lime green with yellow and orange accents. Her outfit lit up the day and I smiled to myself as I made the comparison with her brightness and the dim, darkness of the blacks, browns and navy blues at Mr. Williams' funeral. This woman's attire and her confident approach seemed to wake up the travelers and possibly assist them to face the day in a more positive accepting manner. Her typical message was usually positive and offered hope but with a very definite warning of the necessity and importance of the daily reading of the bible.

As the bus reached the stop where I had exited for more than four years, each of the Domestics I used to walk up and down the hill with either winked, smiled, or threw a kiss to me as they were getting off the bus. They were individually voting for my victory. There had been a buzz on the bus ever since the driver and I had discussed the fact that I was attending Appleton College. Also, Miss TGR was smiling and talking to all of the passengers in her immediate area. It was obvious they were discussing me. In every direction I focused, smiles, an eye wink, an affirmation with the head bobbing up and down or a wind-blown kiss being directed to me. I felt propped up by their acknowledgment.

I realized how much I was representing each of them by attending college, maintaining my very high GPA. Some of them had not graduated from high school and maybe the fact I had been a Domestic and was going to college raised the proverbial bar, gave a new view and gave permission to those who had unhappily settled for a certain position and had never considered other alternatives.

Finally, my point of departure came, I said goodbye to the khaki-clad man and for the first time, an actual smile lit up his face. It alerted me to the fact of the importance of patience and kindness. Standing, awaiting the bus to stop, a multitude of thoughts were racing through my mind. I experienced an unexplainable joy and felt a deep connection and association to those I had crossed the BAILEY with for several years. It was as if I had escaped to a new Me and had no regrets for that person I used to be. My brief thoughts were abruptly halted when I stepped off the bus, as an ambulance was directly in front of our driveway. I almost panicked and began running towards the house. To my relief, Roxanne was standing in the doorway. She explained some teenagers down at the swimming hole were drinking whiskey and one of the girls who had drunk an almost entire bottle had passed out. The adults who had witnessed the incident knew she was okay once the EMT's had revived her. The parents arrived and once they were given the word that she was alright, they willingly accepted the suggestions that she be taken to the hospital in an ambulance wearing an oxygen mask as a deterrent in the hopes she might be frightened enough not to do anything so destructive in the future.

Roxanne and I went into the living room where she interrogated me about my weekend. Playing with my nieces and nephews, visiting some of my neighbors, attending the funeral and spending the delightful time with Barlo the dog was one of the main highlights of the past few days I shared with her. Our conversation focused primarily on the funeral and how people seem to have accepted the notion that unless they display deep sadness and grief they might be judged as disrespectful or as someone who does not care. We compared it to some cultures where rejoicing is the norm when one dies because life is viewed as eternal and death is but a doorway into a different reality. Our connectivity with the All determines how much work is to be done before we evolve to

.

Ninth Chapter

ENHANCED AWARENESS

HAPPINESS IS A CHOICE

Leaning against the door to my bedroom, was a huge package enclosed in a beautiful rose- colored wrapping paper with a huge bow in a contrasting deeper rose. Attached to the package in an envelope was a note with the words, please meet me this evening at 8pm in the Growth Room. I love you and always will. I promise to be respectful and honor you. I removed the wrapping to discover an incredibly large photo of me that had been taken the day of Roxanne's last exhibit. On that day, I had worn a pale, lavender, silk two pieced outfit and the background photograph featured a golden hued sandy beach with a turquoise- blue ocean. It was a photograph of myself, but I must brag, it was stunning.

I rushed to Roxanne to tell her about the note. In her typical manner, she said. "let's have a cup of tea!" The suggestion of having a cup of tea or sitting in the Growth Room were usually what she offered while allowing me to make my own decision. I loved her approach. We drank our tea and ate some of the Fortune Cookies the Chow family had given me. The fortune written on the slip of paper from one of my cookies read, "it's your decision," the other was,"happiness is a choice." Roxanne never shared hers because she became so enthralled by mine. "How prophetic!" she exclaimed. "it is so true, only you get to decide your direction." "But what must I do?" I asked. "Spend some time alone in the Growth Room or if you care to, sit in the garden and keep me company." I did not know what to do.

For a short time, I remained in the Growth Room, then very briefly, I sat in the garden, finally I went inside and took a long shower, I combed and brushed my hair, polished my toenails, lubricated my body, looked at the clock, my effort to go to sleep while attempting to nap failed. Roxanne had taken her shower and informed me that at seven thirty, she was going to dinner and then to a show with a few of her friends. I asked if she really had to go out? She looked at me in her mild manner and said, 'what are you afraid of?" I did not answer, she went out the door and I thought about her question and pondered the idea that maybe I was afraid of myself.

At exactly 8:00pm, Byron announced himself and came in. He handed me a bouquet of orchids and asked if I liked the photograph. I expressed my appreciation and told him how beautiful it was. "Of course! You are beautiful. Let's sit quietly together in the Growth Room." We sat under the pyramid in silence approximately three feet from each other. An interminable amount of time transpired. My anxiety had vanished, I felt safe and comfortable. Almost as if we were guided by forces far beyond description, our hands touched, and we held hands. It was the first time I felt totally at ease with him. Closer and closer we inched towards each other until we were embraced. For a very long time we clung together, no sexual connection, only our hearts and our souls joined. The feeling was beyond my comprehension, it took me to a place I had never ventured before. After a while, we let go of each other, exited the room and he said," I love you and will forever. May I take you to a special place for dinner tomorrow evening?" "Yes," I answered. We embraced again, he went to the door and as he was leaving, "I will see you tomorrow evening, will seven o'clock be alright?" "Yes, that will be fine."

At the exact prearranged time, seven o'clock, the next evening, Byron knocked and entered. He did not proceed beyond the living room. His behavior was tantamount to a teenager being extra polite, being aware of the perimeters when the parents were present or nearby. It was ludicrous when considering that he had been familiar with the obvious as well as the obscure areas of this house since he was ten years old. Reflecting on the gesture, I became aware of his efforts to display a different kind of respect. His efforts to demonstrate his kindness and vulnerability gained my respect. As our relationship became closer, he shared the embarrassment he had felt as he reflected on his aggressive abuse in the past. Remaining in the living room was his desire to start fresh as if ours was a first- time connection.

DARLENE'S AWAKENING

He was sitting on the sofa, as I entered, he stood up, complimented me on my attire and handed me a beautiful jewelry box. "I thought of you when I saw this jewelry box. I want to adorn you with beautiful pieces." When I opened it, there was one of the most beautiful bracelets I had ever seen. It was turquoise with extremely, small inlaid pieces of coral all imbedded in silver. The bracelet was exquisite and had been made by a Hopi Jeweler in northern Arizona. He asked my permission to place it on my wrist. "Yes, you may. I am beginning to feel uncomfortable because you have given me many special gifts and I have never given you anything." "My plan is to treat you as a queen for the rest of our lives, if you will permit me. When I tell you I love you, it is most sincere. The only gifts I need from you are your love."

Roxanne was nowhere to be seen. I began to realize how she is so conveniently absent when Byron arranges to see me. When I ask her for advice, she constantly replies for me to become quiet, use the Growth Room, that is what it is for, listen to yourself and the truth of what you are looking for will always reveal itself. At a different time when Byron and I were having a more serious conversation, he too revealed the almost exact words from Roxanne when she gave him advice. When he was a young boy, he was introduced to the method she recommends and always, he received good results. When he was away at college, there were many times he wished he had access to the Growth Room. Perhaps if he had been able to, some of the past decisions might have been different, but then, we may have never met.

Entering Magnificence, a restaurant I had heard about but having no idea I would ever have had the slightest possibility of going into such a place. It was not too far from the college and having listened to the conversations of some classmates, I assumed it was a very expensive and a popular place for many who were connected to the college. My assumptions were affirmed when as we entered, a very polite hostess approached us, "good evening Mr. Coode, your table is ready." She led us to a table, Byron pulled out my chair for me before I was able to. As we sat at the table, I noticed there was a mixture of people, different races apparently enjoying themselves. What a contrast I was experiencing. Countless times in the past, I had wished for something different, never back then, had I any notion of what was in my future; today; now; at this moment.

Looking around the room, my sense of amazement, happiness, acceptance, forgiveness, words and expressions far away from my limited explanations had engulfed me. He must have sensed my appreciation, because as our eyes met, his face was wearing the biggest smile. "What would you like to drink, he asked?" I was not at all familiar with fancy drinks. The alcoholic beverages I had consumed, had consisted of an occasional beer, or very rarely a glass of wine at a gathering of some kind. For my twenty-first birthday, I sipped tequila, so my alcoholic memories were limited. "Would you like for me to order?" "That will be fine, I replied." He ordered a glass of Chenin Blanc which I drank as we awaited our food. The waiter brought a second glass to accompany our dinner. After our delicious meal consisting of an endive and brie salad, with a pear sauce topping, followed with lobster, asparagus, herbed wild rice and Tiramisu for dessert was completed, The palate pleasing dinner introduced me to a culinary experience I had never known before. Foods offering a first- time pleasure with unforgettable memories.

Byron asked me if I enjoyed jazz music. I was briefly familiar. Anthony had a small jazz collection that he used to play. "Yes, I like some jazz." "I want to take you to a local place around the corner where the music is very good."

We strolled along looking through the windows at most of the shops that were still open. A small bookstore-coffee house with people sitting at tables or standing, there was a typewriter repair shop, a men's clothing store, a smaller shop with a display of magazines, and a menu on the wall offering drinks, salads and sandwiches. The Fashion Zone was the largest of the stores with mannequins dressed in the latest fashions posing in the windows. Byron must have noticed my attraction, when he asked, "Would you like to go in?"   I answered, "Maybe at another time."

Focusing on what the design for my life had been. I realized my ex-community offered no changes and had I remained there, with unquestioned acceptance, I might also have surrendered to a future life of sitting on the porch observing life pass by with no prospects of newness or change.

DARLENE'S AWAKENING

The legacy of slavery had dictated that we very carefully moved about being polite but never being out of step. Those who were somewhat out of step; those who might create waves may experience grave consequences; death, jail or hanging. Possibly there was the thought of change, but who would be the leader? Most Negro citizens I had known stayed on the same path east of the BAILEY which offered a degree of safety and recognizable terrain. Martin Luther King and Malcom X had taken divergent leadership positions during this period. New possibilities were emerging with people of various races, economic realities, religions and cultures supporting these changes.

Learning new models of thought had been experienced and discussed in many of my college classes and my realization had been so stimulated in knowing that I was able to traverse in new directions. Realizing as Byron and I were walking, the close proximity to school this area was and how I had never even permitted an interest to go in the direction north of the school. For too long I had let a robotic posture lead me back and forth with no thought of exploring something new. The college was only three blocks away, and in my almost three and a half years of attending, I had never ventured to this area. Did I represent a people who were so accepting of their dictated roles that they were not willing to do anything which might create disturbances or was the fear so ingrained that remaining in prescribed locations offered an insurance of protection.

As wonderful as Grandma Betty was, she never encouraged me to visit outside our area. Perhaps, it was another of those fear -based legacies inherited from the horrors of slavery. Since I was a child, my life had been so safe east of the BAILEY with very few surprises. Before Anthony and I separated, our non-work enjoyment time was centered in our local community. We never traveled away from our convenient, well-known area. Occasionally, we went to see a movie at The Cameo theater which was located on the main street. Anthony's food preparation was at such a superior level, but from time to time, usually, with a degree of disappointment we would eat at one of the cafes. The large market, beauty and barber shops were centrally located, thereby reducing the need to leave the area. My understanding was most of the people in our community remained there for all necessities. From time to time, a few moved away. Most of the residents stayed all their lives and eventually graduated to a chair on the front porch where they could vicariously have pieces of continuity.

And now, strolling on this street having moved far away from my familiar surroundings everything seemed new and accessible. My thoughts were accelerating so rapidly and the idea that I could have a new life had brought more buoyancy to my stride. Byron asked me again, "are you sure you are okay?" "Yes, yes, yes, I am."

We entered a dimly lit place, The Jazz Spot, with a small stage where four musicians were already engaged in their renditions. There was a bass player so involved in his sounds that he seemed unaware that an audience was present, the drummer kept a steady beat on the drums, the guitar player and the pianist were locked into a fixed duo that was a compliment to the others. Had the ventilation system been better, maybe the cigarette smoke might have been more tolerable; however, after my second glass of wine all complaints seemed to dissipate.

DARLENE'S AWAKENING

Holding on to my stability and not embarrassing myself from having had two glasses of wine with dinner and now two more as I relaxed into the music was more wine than I had ever drunk. The music was exceptionally good; however, having had a first-time experience of drinking four glasses of wine, my objectivity was skewed, and everything was good. Byron was a perfect gentleman, his manner was of respect, patience, and kindness.

Mental exercises, producing inner conflict, reveal uncertainty about the possibility if I would be able to walk the trek back to the parking lot in a dignified way. Slowing down the mental gyrations, reflecting on the grand time the evening had given, remaining in the present and not letting go of Me, I was reassured everything was okay all would be just fine. Byron sat very close, placed his arm around me and I rested my head on his shoulder. The music was good, my stomach was satisfied, the four glasses of wine had given me a warm relaxed feeling and at the precise moment, nothing could have been better. I was beginning to trust him more and more, and my life was beaming with pleasure. The evening's ambience, the food, the music, the wine and his embrace had caused my senses to pirouette beyond the explainable realm leaping into a transcendental reality.

Walking back to the car my feet and legs found their strength; my brain sent the correct messages to me to hold on to my composure and thus all was well. We arrived home and Byron immediately got out of the car, opened my door and asked me if I needed him to help me. I held onto his arm as we walked up the driveway to the front door. My big shock was when he opened the door without attempting to kiss me and asked if we could spend time the entire weekend together. I answered, "yes." The next day he would take me to lunch, and we would spend the rest of the weekend together. Spring Break was a welcomed time which allowed me the pleasure of catching up on many personal obligations. "I will see you at about eleven if that is good." I was ready to be kissed or at least caressed, but he did neither. "Goodnight my love, dream of me." With those words, he turned and walked back to his car. Having had enough wine to warm my wanting was a disappointment when he turned away and rushed back to his car.

I slept very deeply and rose early the next day while mentally preparing for my day together with Byron. When I was not focused on my studies, I realized my mind was occupied with thoughts about Byron.

As I entered the kitchen, Roxanne looked up from her book and expressed her usual beautiful smile. "Good morning my dear. Did you and Byron have a pleasant evening?" I looked at her feeling slightly discomforted, not understanding the reason why. We were both adults nothing happened, even at the time I may have wished something more would have. "Yes," I answered. "It was an excellent evening. First, we went to dinner and for the first time, I ate lobster, it was delicious. After that, we strolled along looking at some of the shops. I had no idea there were such places so close. Finally, we entered The Jazz Spot where the musicians provided excellent music." I then told her of my secret desire not to embarrass myself from having drunk four glasses of wine. She laughed and her face became illuminated with that beautiful signature smile. The satisfaction she revealed was demonstrated in her body language. "Today, he will pick me up at eleven and we will continue our time with each other." "Byron is typically a very good, and decent person. What must have prompted him to take advantage of you continues to puzzle me. That behavior is so uncharacteristic of my nephew."

"My feelings for him are growing more and more. Whenever we are together, he behaves with much respect and kindness for me. Roxanne is the fact that I wanted him to kiss me last night to forward or strange," I asked? "Darlene, you have to be aware of your honest feelings for him or anyone for that matter. My reasoning is that you do not have to wait for him to make the first move, actually he already did several times, even though his approach was very non-conventional. Believe me, I do not take lightly what he did to you. But since the two of you are getting closer, I see no reason you cannot ask for what you want. We have just entered the sixties and many of the notions we have held onto for centuries are dissolving. It is okay to voice what you want. There have been established rules for males and females, I am not saying to reject all the rules, but I do know in wanting equality, it is not just about race and or religion. As a member of the female species, it is important to voice our needs in a way that can be heard. Voicing what our desires are in no way diminishes the roles we have been assigned.

Being aware of time elements, environmental concerns and whatever restrictions present obstacles is one's own personal decision. Do not be fooled by the many gifts Byron has given you. Go deeper into your heart and allow an unobstructed evaluation of what you want or if you want anything from him at all. If you have not already done so, ask yourself all of those questions about what you want from him or what are those things that you do not want. You have shown me some of his correspondence where he speaks about his love for you. Do you share many of the same feelings for him? Until you can truthfully answer some of those questions, you will not be able to move forward."

Quietly I said, "but I do love him. Each time I am with Byron, I realize truthfully and honestly, I really do care very deeply for him, in fact I do love him. When we are not together, I notice my thoughts focus on him much more than I was aware of."

"My husband Phillip and I were married a little over thirty-five years when he had his unfortunate accident. Our marriage was a successful, happy one because of our honesty, commitment to each other, and the deep respect we had for one another. There was nothing we could not discuss. We both felt a responsibility as humans to provide good examples in all that we did. "

As I looked at the clock, I excused myself from Roxanne to be fully prepared for my date with Byron. I was excited to know where we were going and what might unfold this weekend. My curiosity and anxiety forced me to be ready thirty minutes before our agreed upon time. Peering through an opening in the curtains, I was able to see him as he got out of his car and walked up the driveway. I opened the door before he was able to. He smiled in astonishment when I repeated. "You look very handsome." He looked gorgeous. Never had I seen this aspect of Byron. Wearing Jeans, a long -sleeved turtle –neck shirt and tennis shoes was a look I had never seen on him. "Are you ready for an adventurous day?" What were his plans? In a very short span of time, I had begun to have experiences I never would have dreamed of.

Tenth Chapter

WHO AM I ?

The perfect day was unfolding as we rode along listening to music, having polite conversation for an hour and a half on a winding road bordered on both sides with a canopy of trees reaching beyond the explainable. Shorter ones with gnarled trunks, branches barren of leaves suggesting a historical connection of long, long ago.

From this vantage point, I imagined only beauty prevailed, nothing was out of balance, no disharmony, the sun was shining, but not too extreme; the wind was blowing, but not too fierce. From time to time, patterns of cloud formations appeared through the trees and seemed to be in rhythm with the movement of the car. A freedom engulfed me, a lightness that erased jarred memories emerged. A recollection of the innocence of children skipping to their own rhythms where the lightness of heart massages the senses to a state of pure delight. The experience took me outside the physical. A part of me, I was unable to identify had traveled someplace where no description sufficed. My body was attached to the seat, but the non-physical part of me was soaring far away into a mysterious and unexplored realm.

After an impressive drive along a road sculpted by pastures and fields, with a scattering of cattle, horses, goats and sheep we were both surprised when an occasional group of deer were visible.

DARLENE'S AWAKENING

We arrived at a perfectly round cabin sitting high up on a hill from a very impressive lake that extended for several miles to the north. Never would I have imagined a round home. There were no angles, no corners for energies to become lost. The interior of the cabin had a large room with a fireplace, beautiful throw- rugs partially obscuring a hardwood floor, hand woven quilts placed on the two sofas. Roxanne's paintings on the walls blended into the amazing natural ambience that shone through the oversized windows. The art was so delicately perfected, painted and positioned that it was difficult to separate the paintings from the exterior environment. The circular design permitted light to fill each section of the home with an equal amount of brilliance. Windows had been strategically placed to welcome a voluminous amount of sunlight and an unobstructed view of the lake. The three bedrooms and bathrooms were upstairs.

As Byron was unloading the car, he suggested I give myself a tour. Windows in each of the bedrooms were also designed in a way to let more light enter. In addition, they came equipped with a skylight that allowed the night sky to be more revealed. The upstairs rooms had thick carpets that were deep enough to consume the feet with each step.

Byron yelled up to me, "what do you think?" We met on the stairs as I was descending. "What a great place this is. I have never been in a round house before. It somehow feels very different. I am unable to explain, but it does not feel like ordinary houses that are square or rectangular. "

BYRON 1961

He said, "please sit, there are so many important things I need to tell you." We sat down together on the stairs and at first he appeared unable to find the words to express whatever it was he wanted to share with me. He held my hands and looked at me. "Since I was a boy living with my Aunt Lotty, the racial thing has been a bother. My Aunt Lotty was a very dark- skinned woman who I loved more than I can say. At school in our Colored Community, the kids called me Paddy Boy, or Cracker Boy or Whitey. When I came home crying, she repeated those familiar words about sticks and stones. She told me only stupid, ignorant people say things to hurt others. Aunt Lotty told me about times when she was called a Nigger. In the White Community, I listened to horrible pejorative racial slurs. I am grateful for my Negro heritage and my White heritage. The world is so confused regarding racial issues. Being bi-racial, multi-racial whatever the attached label, I have had the opportunity to examine some of the problems more closely. It was with the use of the Pyramid in the Growth Room that I finally discovered who I was and what my values represented.

This home and the home where you live with Roxanne are the locations in which I have spent many good times learning to appreciate all of the aspects of who I am." He paused a moment and continued. "After Janice committed suicide, I sold that monstrosity of a house we had lived in, then came here to work and be alone. Working alone has been an attractive way for me to earn a living, but more recently it has forced me to examine myself a bit more objectively. Arranging schedules based on my time constraints has had much appeal. Fortunately, the success of my work depended entirely on my efforts. Because I had established many dedicated clients, I have always had more work than I could handle. As a Financial Advisor for many successful politicians and high-ranking officials, my record spoke for itself. There have always been constant telephone calls from possible new clients wanting representation. My list of clients has grown continuously and sometimes is more than I can handle. Suggestions that I open a partnership and reduce my client -load have been given, but as demanding as my schedule can be at times, I prefer to work alone. As a student my academic excellence brought about numerous accolades and much recognition. The many college connections I acquired produced an alignment with certain influential people. My career peaked very early and as a result financial instability has never been a consern." And still he continued.

"The conflict for me has always been the lightness of my skin and other physical feature in which many people are unaware of my Negro heritage. Sitting quietly, around dinner tables or at meetings and pretending to enjoy the negative racial innuendos ate away at me in such a way that I developed an ulcer and began therapy. I was supporting racism by not having enough courage to speak up. Each time a despicable racial slur was referenced my stomach began to hurt. I had been taught to have respect for all people regardless of their ethnic, racial or religious identity. When I was given the opportunity as an adult man, I sat quietly in order to close a deal." Again, Byron slowed down his delivery; however, this time, he removed a handkerchief from his pocket and wiped away tears as he spoke, "I realized the shame I might have caused auntie Roxanne and Uncle Phillip who had taught me better. In counseling sessions, I faced up and admitted the betrayal of Lotty, my Aunt who had raised me and died when I was ten. To betray her, who had cared so much and sacrificed everything for me, prompted me to ask, what kind of person was I? I had begun to hate myself so much that I was unable to look at myself in a mirror. In this world, it was easier to have white skin, but as I questioned more and more my deceit, I hated the person I had become. Was it all because of the impressive amount of money I was earning or was it because of a desire to not identify as a Negro?

I had begun to lose all respect for myself and Janice who I was forced to marry based on the lie that I had impregnated her. But once the truth about the pregnancy was revealed, our relationship was dismantled. We remained married to present a unified image. We shared a home, but almost nothing else unless we were forced to. Most of my time was away from home or in my office. Therapy has helped me realize the degree of dysfunction our marriage epitomized.

Byron's, words were spitting out with the rapidity of a rocket.as if he were unable to hold back; as if he had been thinking and thinking about the need to share with me everything he had ever thought about. Spewing out words with very little breath in between his delivery.

DARLENE'S AWAKENING

"My therapist must have had a degree of agitation based on the problems I brought him. My inability to openly acknowledge my Negro heritage, my wife's suicide, my abusive bullying of you, a person I had vibrant and loving images of from my dreams. Was I losing my mind? Sitting in the Growth Room and coming to an awareness is what has finally made me accept the realization of who I am and who I have been. Again, I ask you to please forgive me, please, please accept my sincerest apology. I am so sorry to have treated you in such a disrespectful way, I am not that kind of person. In retrospect, each time I abused you, my lack of self-respect, my lack of respect for you became lost. I let a selfish desire take control without regard for your feelings. All that mattered at the time was how good I was made to feel. Please, again I ask you to know that is not the person I am. Despite some of my dysfunctions, my childhood was a happy one. There are wonderful memories and I remember great times before Uncle Phillip died. He used to take me hiking into some of the wooded areas around here. We used to fish together. One time, we decided to only eat the foods we gathered. On that particular day, we ate fish, some kinds of algae that he was familiar with. We gathered wild lettuce, berries, onions and a few other wild greens. He dug up some roots, but I have no recollection as to what they may have been. As we sat quietly, Uncle Phil talked to me about the responsibilities and challenges I needed to be aware of. He spoke to me about racism, self-love and mutual respect. Things we shared about the importance of becoming a real man.

In those counseling sessions, I came face to face with who I had become. I knew in order to respect and like myself, it was necessary to make some immediate changes. What I do recall were those good memories my uncle and I shared. I refuse to let go of them. My uncle Phillip was a good example of the kind of man I have patterned my life after. Realizing what a disappointment I had become was another reason I had to represent myself as a man with decent values. It was the main reason I began therapy in order to acquire some help to lead me back on a more humane path and reconsider the choices I had grown accustomed to accepting.

In addition to the Growth Room, this location is where I have spent large amounts of time when attempting to resolve some of my troublesome puzzles. Life has at times been difficult, but because of Auntie Lotty, Uncle Phillip and Aunt Roxanne, I have held on. I knew there would be a day, I would meet the one of my dreams and when finally you entered my life, I realized all would be resolved in a positive way." Again, he took out his handkerchief and wiped away tears that were running down his cheeks.

In spite of all the perplexities of my life, I can admit that I am pleased with who I have become. My racial Identity: Colored, White, Negro, Caucasian, Black is a very small part of who I really am.

I assumed his sharing of the many pent-up frustrations and the embarrassment he had suffered must have been cathartic, because he had talked incessantly without a pause. Finally, he asked, "are you hungry or thirsty? Please feel free to treat this place as your home. There is plenty of food in the refrigerator, beverages of all kinds."

AWAKENING

From somewhere in the ethers, I was coyly surprised when I heard myself say, "Byron, would you please stop talking and kiss me?" He was as stunned as I. "What did you say?" Why did he have to make me repeat it?" Carefully and with much determination I asked. "Would you just kiss me?" Without any further interruptions, he grabbed me and I surrendered. The kiss unlocked a blockage that had been bolted for the past few years, boulders dissolved beyond recognition. Uninvited obstructions succumbed to a bottomless abyss, parts of me reunited in a dance of unparalleled delight. Both of my arms, I placed gently and securely around his neck, pressed my body into his and kissed him as if I had never kissed or been kissed before. My body experienced pleasure that was beyond description. Our kiss ended slowly, we looked at each other as if it were the first time. "I love you more and more he said."

He turned away from me and said he was going down to the lake. Why did he have to leave just at the moment I had found enough courage to take control of my wants? I watched him through the window as he headed to the lake. His venture to the water was extremely brief. I watched as he turned around and almost ran back to the house. Byron reentered and came directly to where I was. Rapidly breathing, he took a breath and said, "The fact that you initiated our first real kiss was what I have wanted, it was what I have asked for. It took me so off guard that my foundation was shaky. Our relationship has advanced to a different octave. I had been the one who had dictated the moves without obtaining your permission. Today, you took complete control and even asked me if I would kiss you. What you did was so powerful and caught me so off guard that I was taken to a place where I was surprisingly unprepared. For a time, I found myself lost in the recesses of my mind floating in an alien existence searching for sustainability. I rushed out of the house to get my bearings. I love you more than I know how to express. I promise to never be the aggressor again, to never ever hurt you and to be able to offer you pleasure when you desire. Please tell me you will marry me."

I will, I love you." The words escaped before I was able to examine or censor them. He removed an exquisitely, magnificent, handcrafted ring from his pocket, unlike any I had ever seen and placed it on my finger. It was an emerald surrounded by chips of sapphires. He explained that it was not the typical engagement ring made of diamonds that most people wear. He did not want to support the diamond industry where so many African people were exploited, even though he was aware some of the miners who dig for the emeralds were also treated poorly.

He picked me up and we kissed. I then asked him to make love to me. I was only interested in lovemaking, not a sexual encounter. In the exact spot where we were, we melted into the floor; we made love for the very first time. There was an electrical current igniting, titillating, charging, touching and embracing every cell in my body. When we were hungry, we ate, we discussed our wants, our past hurts, and in addition to being lovers, we became friends with a fresh, cleansed togetherness that we recognized for the first time. After eating we made love again. It was as if we had never witnessed each other before these times. Intense cellular stimulation detonating an energy force that catapulted us beyond the explainable. Our bodies were suspended as we floated down to the lake. We had entered a dimension where only our souls, our spirits connected. We touched and sparks were released that brightened our path. On the soft ground heated by the sun in a private area near the lake our lovemaking resumed. Returning to the house making love as we were showering, soothed and satisfied my profound wanting.

DARLENE'S AWAKENING

Byron had brought more than enough food for all of our meals. There was an abundance of everything. The delicious dinner that satisfied our hunger had been an interruption of our single mind objective. The dishes were washed, the kitchen was cleaned and again we shared the mysteriously, magical love connection. The realization that we were so perfectly fitted to each other created a magnetic field that could not be drawn apart. Sleep escaped us that weekend. The lovemaking we each contributed reflected our souls recognizing their commonalities. A more beautiful, sensual and satisfying experience I hadn't known was possible. A few breaks we had, but for two days our lovemaking did not stop, it was a continuous unfolding. We discussed every possible future apprehension we could think of that might erupt because of our contrasting physical appearances. At a depth far below the surface on an invisible level, we became aware that there were no obstacles strong enough to weaken our connection.

Expressing myself clearly and to the point, tools I had gained in some of my college classes. My ability to ask for love was a new approach. I looked at myself in the mirror and became acquainted with a new person whom I liked and admired. At twenty-six years old, I had fallen in love again. I had been celibate for approximately four and a half years. A new receptivity of lovemaking had soothed me and offered acknowledgment of a recurring transition. Very slowly I had allowed this relationship to develop. My heart had become more accepting, other parts of my being had relaxed, resulting in joy becoming my norm. I was in love again and it was equally shared. It was a more adult relationship with a reciprocal exchange.

On Monday when we returned home from our amazingly, delightfully love-filled weekend. My last quarter of classes resumed. At the end of this session, I will have earned a Bachelor of Arts Degree with a focus on Social Systems and Peace Studies.

Three days after we returned home, we had a simple marriage ceremony where Lorna, Larcel, their kids and Roxanne attended. Byron and I officially, and legally became Mr. and Mrs. We have promised to have a real honeymoon at a future time; however, remembering the time we spent the weekend together in the circular cabin was for me a glorious honeymoon before the marriage. It was a special time that cannot be duplicated.

A marriage, a graduation, the discovery that I was pregnant and the arrival of our child in early January, all new developments within a few months of each other were beyond what I would have imagined a short while ago when I used to ride the early morning bus from the east across the BAILEY to the west. I realized the importance of being extremely direct and completely focused when I make requests to the Universe for changes. I used to hope for something different not knowing the power of my thoughts, my desires, my wishes which have been granted. The All- Knowing Source which is apparently always available, Grandmother Betty or some force in the Universe beyond my comprehension certainly had paid homage to my requests and I have continually offered gratitude.

Byron had been living in an extremely small one-bedroom apartment with two very long tables that were strewn with his multitude of documents and an assortment of stacked boxes allowing a very limited area to move about. Roxanne reminded us of the large available space that her home provided and insisted that as a family we remain living in her home with her. She smiled when she said, "you are my children and I am overjoyed to know that I have a grandchild who will soon be making an appearance."

Happiness seemed to be her constant identification. Was it because of the energetic nature emanated from the pyramid she had lived with for such a long time or was it because she was naturally a kind, loving, open hearted individual?

The fact that people around the world from all different groups share similarities has been a revelation. Remaining sheltered in my comfortably, recognizable community, I may never have learned about the countless details we all have in common. Experiences at Appleton, the probing perspectives from my first husband Anthony, the love and vulnerability Byron has shared, continuous teachings from Grandmother Betty and the amazing examples from Roxanne have taught me well.

DARLENE'S AWAKENING

Realizing the importance of having objective inquiry, experiencing more quiet, always respecting oneself and others, being joyful and maybe solutions to the many challenges that appear as we go through life searching for our unique identities will be more available.

Even though Roxanne and I were not biologically connected, there is a special connection we have, as if our blood ties shared the same DNA. From the first encounter we had, there was an undeniable link that locked us together. Our relationship goes beyond the boundaries of racial identification. We have connected as family members and the love we share for each other traverses the boundaries of those limiting characteristics which tend to separate us as a human species. I love her the way in which I loved my Mama Betty.

Such revelations many people never have opportunities to become aware of. Living in her home, our home, had an aura of Light that welcomed love, stability and satisfaction. Roxanne had become so interested in the proposed arrival of our baby that she had begun purchasing baby clothes and an assortment of other useful items. She had asked our permission to alter one of the rooms into a nursery. What a gift for us to know that Roxanne will be the grandmother of our children.

My experiences as a young Negro female have been anything but average, typical or ordinary. Many of the defining moments in my life have had their own unique unfolding. I ask myself do I have a certain degree of responsibility to alert others of the possible unexpected adventures that lie in wait? As this thought has entered my awareness, I am again reminded that we each have our own particular direction. Perhaps, the most I can do is to constantly attempt to be a good example.

Some of the personal highlights of my life are what have been shared with you. Byron and I have been married four years and are the parents of two children, Imelda the older who is three and was named after my mother of whom I have no recollection of and our one and a half-year -old son, Tyler.

The accelerated plan I was accepted into will award me my master's degree two months from now. Plans for my future have not been fully decided; however, if I choose a different path from being an available parent, I will be prepared. Those degrees I have earned are an offering to Grandma, Mama Betty and the light she saw coming through. Thanks to Roxanne and Byron, I have been exposed to educational opportunities that were foreign to me and may have remained that way forever.

There are people who have come to the realization that equality and justice were essential for the betterment of society. Even though the Civil Rights Movement was having a profound effect on the population and integration was beginning to be the norm in many areas of society it was still quite difficult for some of Byron's clients with their narrow, slanted perspectives to utilize his services as their financial representative once they discovered he married a Negro, a Colored woman. His opinion was that for too long he quietly accepted their hatred and unjust behaviors when their racial biases manifested.

His ability to state to some clients that he was no longer able to represent them has enabled him to stand taller and appreciate the person he has grown into. The number of demands for Byron's services usually exceeded his ability. According to him, because he has become more selective with whom he has chosen to work with, he is now able to look at himself in a mirror without shame and has gained the ability to have more self-respect.

Byron has been volunteering at a center for males who were abused and those who have been abusers. Redirecting some of the males to brighter, more-life affirming directions and assisting them to make better choices, he has been able to help many of them. His role as a strong male who is willing to listen, offer compassion and patience causes the telephone to ring non-stop. On different occasions, I have been asked to tell my story. The two of us have been invited to many sites where we share our stories about aggression, bullying, victimization, resolution and forgiveness.

We are constantly counting the many rewards that have come to us. My husband and I remain the best of friends. He still calls me his queen as he constantly adorns me with surprises.

With an increased understanding of my involvement and responsibility to fulfill that which makes for a better world, that which promotes more understanding, I have gained a very deep respect for continuously acquiring as much awareness as I am able to and knowing that learning, and evolving and awakening is a life-long process. The palate that has symbolized me has been painted with varying shades of beauty and lightness which has overshadowed any cluttered obscurations. My exposure to new concepts, new cultures, and openings into possibilities that appeared as far-away dreams out of my reach have become real and totally accessible.

Arriving at the realization that a force governed by the Source which represents harmony, balance and true happiness is always available to me. As I continue in my practice of Quietness, a new awareness manifests and solutions become more accessible. Essential components on the path to Awakening are the tools of forgiveness and respect of oneself and others.

To be loved, to offer love is a necessity for peace and harmony to exist on our very challenging planet we call Earth. ....

A CONCLUSION

NEWLY REALIZED SELF

seasons change alerting me to the discovery of awaiting horizons
summer's sun shines through stagnation in my perceived blockages
autumn breezes blow away doubt left by confused memories
appearances that dismay my authenticity i reject... shackles that
bound me release their hold.... negative influences are dispelled
observations fluctuate as a mist covers my longing for clarity
evening stars vanish into timeless realms, today and tomorrow
merge
changes in my perception alarm non-essentials clinging tightly
a realization of my significance alerts me to a wonderment
true aspects of my consciousness are all that remain
summoned by a force offering no apologies
where the now and the forever remain attached
my clarity evolves and my joy expands
the dance of forever leaps into an unexplained brilliance
a new recognizable self emerges
i step forward into sunlight's radiance

\	FAMILY AND FRIENDS

APPRECIATION FOR YOUR KINDNESS AND ASSISTANCE, I
OFFER UNLIMITED GRATITUDE..................

Kent Manzi Grant
Roxanne Lawson
Desire Morales
Sandra Shawhan
Regina Jones
Ruth Anne Auten
Jeanne Freeman
Shelby Jones
Valerie Lasciak
Pamela Wai'olena
Selimah Nemoy

Ida Nell Barnett
Channa Grace
Tagi Gorg
Gentry Gorg
Cheayenne Gorg
Karimah Gorg
Carter and Christina Gorg
Richard Orion Gorg-Coleman
Richard Coleman

THE AUTHOR

Gwyndolin Gorg grew up in Los Angeles, California where she was given opportunities to view the world from a much different perspective than her parents who had grown up in Texas in the early forties. Ms. Gorg has worked professionally for more than fifty years as an actress, model, dancer, singer, songwriter, storyteller, screenwriter, producer, director, educator and theatre manager. Her work has been in; television, radio, film and educational media.

As an educator, she has taught from kindergarten to college level in private and public schools. Ms. Gorg has always been involved in the growth and development of younger people.

She and her husband worked with the Traditional Indian Land and Life Committee to assist Native Americans defray their court costs. As a result of their involvement, with a group of Traditional Hopi in Oraibi, Arizona extended an invitation for them to remain in one of the Pueblos while making the award- winning documentary, Autobiography of a Hopi.

Ms. Gorg served as the educational coordinator of the 18th Street Arts Complex in Santa Monica, California. She is a 2002-2003 grant's winner of the California Arts Council. In 2007-2008 Ms. Gorg won the teacher of the year award, presented by the United Teachers of Los Angeles. At the International House of Blues, Hollywood, she co-created the Blues Schoolhouse Program as a performing artist and history consultant.

In Hawaii, Ms. Gorg was appointed resident artist in the schools by the Hawaii State Department. She co-founded the Hilo Theatre for youth, a theatrical performance company in Hawaii. At Leeward College in Honolulu, she wrote produced, directed and hosted the Oahu Gazette, a community television magazine show for Public Broadcasting Service.

A film documentary that she co-wrote and produced with her husband, Inside State Prison about Penitentiary in Honolulu, won special Honors at the Los Angeles International Film Exhibition (FILMEX). Her films, Autobiography of a Hopi, won many awards at various Film Festivals.

Ms.Gorg wrote and produced the Savages, an educational documentary about juvenile street gangs in Venice, California which won Honors at the Columbus Film Festival and the American Film Festival. Her entertainment feature film writing and producing credits include Living the Blues, starring the legendary Sam Taylor, which was winner of a Filmtrax award at Belgium's Ghent International Film Festival. Gwyndolin Gorg is a graduate of Hawaii Pacific University.

At Maui Language Institute at the University of Hawaii, she was an instructor for eight years. She is the Executive Producer for Media Associates Production Company. African Americans on Maui Association which promotes inclusivity of all peoples in the hope of making our world a more harmonious place is where she served as President for nine years. I AM THE BLUES, NICE LADY (a lighter approach to Alzheimers), I AM BIGGER THAN NIGGER are three of her works.

Ms Gorg, recently widowed, makes her home in Hawaii with her children and grandchildren,

Made in the USA
Columbia, SC
18 July 2021